Government Simulations and Debates

Glencoe
McGraw-Hill

New York, New York   Columbus, Ohio   Woodland Hills, California   Peoria, Illinois

To the Teacher

As educators have long known and research has supported, student participation in the government classroom—like citizen participation in our government—is the key to successful learning. On the following pages, you will find a variety of ways to give your students valuable, memorable, and pedagogically sound hands-on learning experiences that reinforce fundamental concepts of government.

The two proven techniques chosen for inclusion in this booklet are those of simulations and debates. Simulations have the inherent value of giving students as close to a real-world experience of government as is possible in the classroom. The value of student debates lies in the research, logical thinking, and presentation skills necessary for the debates to take place.

This booklet includes all the necessary teacher guidelines and student activity sheets for nine simulations and nine debates, one of each keyed to each unit in *United States Government: Democracy In Action*.

The McGraw·Hill Companies

Send all inquiries to:
Glencoe/McGraw-Hill
8787 Orion Place
Columbus, Ohio 43240

ISBN 0-07-873070-8

Printed in the United States of America

4 5 6 7 8 9 10 045 09 08

Customize Your Resources

No matter how you organize your teaching resources, Glencoe has what you need.

The Teacher's Classroom Resources for *United States Government: Democracy In Action* provides you with a wide variety of supplemental materials to enhance the classroom experience. These resources appear as individual booklets in a carryall tote box. The booklets are designed to open flat so that pages can be easily photocopied without removing them from their booklet. However, if you choose to create separate files, the pages are perforated for easy removal. You may customize these materials using our file folders or tabbed dividers.

The individual booklets and the file management kit supplied in Teacher's Classroom Resources give you the flexibility to organize these resources in a combination that best suits your teaching style. Below are several alternatives:

- Organize all resources by category
  (all tests, all enrichment and enhancement activities, all cooperative learning activities, etc., filed separately)
- Organize all resources by category and chapter
  (all Chapter 1 activities, all Chapter 1 tests, etc.)
- Organize resources sequentially by lesson
  (activities, quizzes, readings, etc., for Chapter 1, Chapter 2, and so on)

Table of Contents

Government Simulations and Debates

★ UNIT 1 Foundations of American Government

★ UNIT 2 The Legislative Branch

★ UNIT 3 The Executive Branch

★ UNIT 4 The Judicial Branch

Conducting the Debates

From unfunded mandates to the use of American military force, the nine debates in this booklet are designed to help you address current, compelling issues in the context of learning about the American government.

Although they address a wide variety of topics, each of the nine debates follows this basic format:

Introduce the Issue: The debate topic is introduced, and teams are presented with a resolution to debate.

Learn About the Issue: Team members conduct research to learn about the debate topic and identify and develop arguments and evidence for both sides of the resolution.

Debate the Issue: Teams decide on the order of speakers and conduct the debate.

Reflect on the Issue: Team members and audience members think and write about the debate topic, explore it on a larger level, and conduct an activity to extend their learning.

Participating in the Debates For each debate, organize two teams: an affirmative team, which will support the resolution, and a negative team, which will oppose it. Each team can consist of an individual, two members (one making the presentation, the other conducting the cross examination and giving the rebuttal), or three members (one making the presentation, one conducting the cross-examination, and one giving the rebuttal).

The following is a suggested debate format:

1. affirmative presentation (5 minutes): affirmative speaker presents prepared speech arguing for resolution

2. cross-examination (2 minutes): negative speaker asks questions of affirmative speaker

3. negative presentation (5 minutes): negative speaker presents prepared speech arguing against resolution

4. cross-examination (2 minutes): affirmative speaker asks questions of negative speaker

5. negative rebuttal (3 minutes): negative speaker refutes affirmative arguments

6. affirmative rebuttal (3 minutes): affirmative speaker refutes negative arguments

7. class questions (10 minutes): class asks questions of both sides

8. class vote to determine the winner (optional)

Name _____ Date _____ Class _____

Government Simulations and Debates

Debate 1: Easier Constitutional Amendments?

As the supreme law of the land, the Constitution established the ideals of the country and the structure of government. Because the Framers knew the Constitution might need to change to meet the needs of a growing nation, they established a mechanism for amending the Constitution.

They intended that amendments be considered deliberately and completely, and as a result they made the amendment process slow and somewhat difficult. Today, however, many Americans argue that amending the Constitution is too cumbersome and necessary, worthwhile amendments are virtually impossible to ratify. They want to streamline the process. Their opponents argue that the current system is valuable and should remain in place.

DIRECTIONS Complete the steps below to learn about both sides of this issue. You will debate this resolution:

Resolved: The constitutional amendment process should be streamlined.

Step 1. **Learn About the Issue** Consult your textbook, magazine, and newspaper articles in order to understand the current amendment process and to investigate the history of amendments that have been proposed. Examine both those that have been ratified and those that have failed, such as the Equal Rights Amendment and the Balanced Budget Amendment.

Identify reasons both for and against the debate resolution. Use the chart in the front of this book to help organize your research. Then develop at least three arguments for streamlining the amendment process and three arguments against it. As you develop the arguments, record the statistics, quotations, and other evidence that supports them and develop responses or refutations to the arguments on both sides.

Step 2. **Debate the Issue** Once you have completed your research, proceed with the debate. Organize two teams: an affirmative team to support the resolution and a negative team to oppose it. The debate will consist of presentations, questions, and rebuttals. Refer to page vi in the front of this booklet for a description of the debate format.

Step 3. **Reflect on the Issue**

DIRECTIONS On a separate sheet of paper complete the following:

1. Write a paragraph reflecting your personal opinion about streamlining the amendment process and explaining the reasons for your position.

2. A proposed amendment may be ratified in one of two ways. Of the 26 amendments, all but one has been ratified by the same method. Which method was it? Why do you think this method was used? Conduct research to find the answers.

3. **Activity:** Write an amendment you think should be added to the Constitution. Include a discussion of the arguments for its ratification.

Simulation 1: Teacher Strategy

ESTABLISHING A GOVERNMENT

In this simulation, students will simulate this scenario: stranded on a deserted island, they must design and establish a government for themselves.

PURPOSE ★ ★ ★ ★ ★ ★ ★ ★ ★ ★ ★ ★ ★ ★ ★ ★ ★

For students, the simple, basic purposes and types of government are often obscured by the unique aspects of the hundreds of governments in the world that have evolved in particular cultural, historical, and economic circumstances. In this simulation, many of these variables are eliminated, enabling students to focus on basic issues of governmental purposes and types.

OBJECTIVES ★ ★ ★ ★ ★ ★ ★ ★ ★ ★ ★ ★ ★ ★ ★

By participating in this simulation, students will:
• identify the main purposes of government
• compare the advantages and disadvantages of different types of government
• develop their own government

TIME REQUIRED ★ ★ ★ ★ ★ ★ ★ ★ ★ ★ ★ ★ ★

This simulation activity is designed to be conducted over the course of one week (five class periods, plus out-of-class preparation time), in conjunction with student reading and studying of fundamental ideas of government and the formation of the American government. You can abbreviate the time, but consider devoting at least two class periods to the simulation to allow adequate preparation, participation, and evaluation time.

MATERIALS ★ ★ ★ ★ ★ ★ ★ ★ ★ ★ ★ ★ ★ ★ ★

• Student copies of Activity Sheets 1A, 1B, 1C, 1D, and 1E
• Folders

TEACHING TIPS ★ ★ ★ ★ ★ ★ ★ ★ ★ ★ ★ ★ ★

• Ensure that different students propose different types of government, so that the debate in the simulation gives them the opportunity to compare and contrast the advantages and disadvantages of different approaches to government.

• Emphasize the parallels between the challenges the students face in the simulation and the challenges the Founders of the U.S. government faced.

PROCEDURE ★ ★ ★ ★ ★ ★ ★ ★ ★ ★ ★ ★ ★ ★ ★

Introduce the Simulation Use Activity Sheet 1A (Background Brief) as the basis for this lesson. Make sure that students understand the scenario. Urge them to begin thinking about the real problems facing such a group of castaways. Many students are familiar with William Golding's 1955 novel *Lord of the Flies*, in which a group of boys faces a similar situation.

Prepare for the Simulation Use Activity Sheet 1B (Preparing for the Simulation) as the basis for this lesson. Focus students' attention on the basic question they must answer in Step 4: What *type* of government would best achieve the *purposes* of government in *this situation*? Consider distributing Activity Sheet 1C (Conducting the Simulation) in advance to help students prepare.

Conduct the Simulation Use Activity Sheets 1C (Conducting the Simulation) and 1E as the basis for this lesson. There are two ways to conduct this simulation. You may choose to organize students into separate "islands," having each develop their own form of government, and compare and contrast the results. Or, have all the students participate in a single simulation.

Review the Simulation Use Activity Sheet 1D as the basis for this lesson. This sheet functions well as a homework activity, or you can use it as a guide for a classroom discussion. You may also choose to evaluate individual student work on the other activity sheets.

Government Simulations and Debates

Simulation 1: Establishing a Government

⭐ **DIRECTIONS** ➤ You will participate in a simulation in which you design and establish a government for you and your classmates. To help you prepare, read the Background Brief. Then answer the questions.

★ ★ ★ ★ ★ ★ ★ ★ ★ ★ ★ ★ ★ ★ ★ ★ ★ **Background Brief** ★ ★ ★ ★ ★ ★ ★ ★ ★ ★ ★ ★ ★ ★ ★ ★

As the smoke clears, you take stock of the situation.

Your plane has crash-landed. Just a few minutes before the crash, you and your fellow students had been flying high over the Pacific, on your way to Japan to participate in an exchange program. Then something went terribly wrong, and the pilot was forced to land on a small and remote island. Some students are injured and require care. As they are attended to, others set out to explore the island. A few hours is enough to see all the island has to offer. There is a clear spring for water, and plenty of wild fruits, vegetables, and game. There are trees for firewood and building shelter. The plane is in pretty good shape, and your group is able to salvage much—first-aid kits, clothing, and so on—from the wreckage. So far so good. "We can survive here," you think to yourselves.

There's bad news too. The pilot informs you that he was off course: he's unsure of your location. Worse, because the crash happened so quickly, he didn't have time to issue a distress signal. The radio was destroyed in the crash. The news sinks in: you may all be here for a very long time.

Motivated by your common need for survival, you cooperate: one group builds crude shelters, while another gathers food. After a few days of steady work, everyone is comfortable. After a few weeks, a routine has settled in.

The first sign of trouble comes from one student who refuses to take his turn to collect water from the spring. Other students support him. They wander off, refusing to do the work necessary for survival on the island. A few students start to build a boat, hoping to sail to safety. It's just big enough for themselves. Another group begins to build its own shelters on the far side of the island; they are planning to establish a separate community. The different groups of students begin to compete for the island's dwindling resources. Your once cohesive group is splitting up.

If something is not done, disaster will result. It is clear that you need rules to govern your group. You need a code of conduct. You need a common purpose. You will have to create a government.

★ ★

1. Explain why you and your classmates would need a government in this situation.

2. Given this situation, how do you think you should go about the process of creating a government?

Government Simulations and Debates

Simulation 1: Establishing a Government

DIRECTIONS In this simulation you will imagine yourself and your classmates stranded on a deserted island, forced to design and establish a government for yourselves. To prepare for this simulation, complete the steps below.

Step 1. Prepare a Simulation Folder Use a folder to organize the various papers you will need for your simulation. Your folder should include any activity sheets your teacher hands out (such as this one), research materials, and notes you take. Update your folder as you proceed.

Step 2. Identify the Purposes of a Government To establish a government, you'll need to know *why* governments are created. To help you, list the four major purposes of government in the chart below. For each, give an example of how a government fulfills that purpose.

PURPOSES OF GOVERNMENT	EXAMPLES
1.	
2.	
3.	
4.	

Step 3. Understand the Three Basic Types of Government To establish a government, you'll need to decide what *type* of government to create. To help you, list the three basic types of government in the chart below. Briefly describe each one.

TYPES OF GOVERNMENT	DESCRIPTION

Step 4. Decide on Your Position Review the charts you completed in Steps 2 and 3. Keep them in mind as you think about your situation on the island. Ask yourself this basic question: What *type* of government would best achieve the *purposes* of government in *this situation*? When you have decided, write your answer on a separate sheet of paper. Make sure you identify the reasons for your decision—you're going to need them to try to convince your classmates.

Name _____ Date _____ Class _____

Government Simulations and Debates

Simulation 1: Establishing a Government

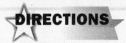 **DIRECTIONS** In this simulation you will experience the thought and cooperation required to design and establish a government. You must meet to form a government for your stranded group. Use the space below each step to take notes during the simulation.

Step 1. **Meet and Decide** Each student should present the type of government he or she thinks is best suited to the situation, making sure to explain the reasons for his or her position. The reasons should explain how the *type* of government being proposed is best suited to fulfilling the *purposes* of government, given the situation on the island. Once everyone has spoken, debate the various positions and proposals. You should feel free to challenge other students' positions. Ask questions, point out problems, and argue your position. On the other hand, you should also be open to accepting other positions, or modifying your own, if others' arguments are convincing.

_____

_____

_____

_____

Step 2. **Draft a Constitution** Once you have reached a decision on what type of government to establish, draft a simple constitution to establish your government officially and to describe its most important features. Your constitution must fulfill all of the basic purposes of constitutions.

_____

_____

_____

_____

Step 3. **Revise the Constitution** The language of a constitution is of paramount importance. Carefully revise your constitution to avoid inconsistencies and confusion, which might lead to conflicts among citizens.

_____

_____

_____

_____

Government Simulations and Debates

Simulation 1: Establishing a Government

DIRECTIONS Think carefully about your experience in the simulation as you answer the questions below.

The Simulation ★

1. What was the best thing about the simulation? What was the worse thing about it? Explain your answers.

_____

_____

_____

2. Evaluate the realism of your simulation. In other words, how realistic was the situation, the meeting, and

your responses? _____

_____

_____

3. What were the major issues you had to resolve in order to establish a government? List them below. Next to each, explain how it was similar to a problem faced by the Founders of the U.S. government.

_____

_____

_____

Your Role in the Simulation ★

4. How well do you think you performed your role in the simulation? Could you have done anything better?

Explain your answer. _____

_____

5. Identify the three most important things you learned from participating in this simulation.

- _____

- _____

- _____

6. Write a brief paragraph that explains how this simulation helped you learn more about the U.S.

government. _____

_____

_____

Government Simulations and Debates

Activity Sheet 1E

Simulation 1: Establishing a Government

⭐**DIRECTIONS** The diagram identifies the major purposes of a Constitution. The constitution you create should fulfill each of these purposes. Complete the diagram to identify how the U.S. Constitution fulfills each purpose. Then create another diagram as you draft your own constitution. Show how your constitution fulfills each purpose.

IDENTIFIES GOALS AND PURPOSES IN A PREAMBLE

PROVIDES FOR THE RESOLUTION OF DISPUTES

SETS FORTH THE IDEALS OF THE GROUP

PROVIDES FOR THE ENFORCEMENT OF THE LAW

Major Purposes of a Constitution

ESTABLISHES BASIC STRUCTURE OF GOVERNMENT

PROVIDES THE SUPREME LAW AND PRINCIPLES

DEFINES THE GOVERNMENT'S POWERS

PROVIDES FOR THE SELECTION OF OFFICIALS

Name _____ Date _____ Class _____

Debate 2: Should Members of Congress Face Term Limits?

Congress has always been the scene of passionate debates, on everything from federal spending to environmental legislation. But one of the most hotly debated issues is unlike any other: it concerns the debaters themselves.

The question concerns how long individuals should be allowed to remain in Congress.

Currently, there are no limits to the number of terms members of Congress can serve. As a result, many in Congress have managed to remain in office for extremely long periods of time—even decades. A large number of Americans want to change that by imposing congressional term limits.

DIRECTIONS Complete the steps below to learn about both sides of this issue. You will research and debate this resolution:

Resolved: Congressional term limits should be enacted.

Step 1. **Learn About the Issue** Begin by conducting research about term limits. You will consult your textbook, magazine and newspaper articles, and other appropriate resources. Your goal is to find at least three arguments for congressional term limits and three arguments against them. The chart on page 1 will help organize your research. As you identify each argument, make sure you note supporting statistics, quotations, and other evidence. You should also develop rebuttals to both sides of the argument.

Step 2. **Debate the Issues** Once you have completed your research, you are ready to proceed with the debate. Organize two teams: a supporting team that will answer yes to the debate question and an opposing team that will answer no. The debate will consist of presentations, questions, and rebuttals. Refer to page vi in the front of this booklet for a description of the debate format.

Step 3. **Reflect on the Issue**

DIRECTIONS On a separate sheet of paper, complete the following:

1. Write a paragraph that identifies your opinion about term limits and explain the reasons for your position.

2. Find out which current member of Congress has served the longest. Also find out who holds the record for the most terms.

3. **Activity:** Discuss this question with your classmates: why do incumbent members of Congress tend to oppose term limits?

Simulation 2: Teacher Strategy

A CONGRESSIONAL COMMITTEE HEARING

In this simulation students will assume the roles of the principals in a congressional committee hearing.

PURPOSE ★★★★★★★★★★★★★★★★★★

The most public and political aspect of committee work is the committee hearing. Students will gain a more thorough understanding of the fundamentals of congressional committee hearings, the functions of the federal government, and media reports of committee hearings.

OBJECTIVES ★★★★★★★★★★★★★★★

By participating in this simulation, students will:
- identify the central role of committees
- analyze the information-gathering process
- investigate the advantages and disadvantages of the committee system

TIME REQUIRED ★★★★★★★★★★★★★

This simulation activity is designed to be conducted over the course of one week (five class periods, plus out-of-class preparation time). You can abbreviate the time required by doing much of the preparatory work yourself. Consider devoting at least two class periods to the simulation.

MATERIALS ★★★★★★★★★★★★★★★★★

- Student copies of Activity Sheets 2A, 2B, 2C, 2D, and 2E
- Folders
- Appropriate research materials
- Costumes and props: for example, students may wear dress clothes and use props such as charts for presentation to the committee.

TEACHING TIPS ★★★★★★★★★★★★★

- Choosing an appropriate committee and bill for students to consider is critical to a successful simulation. Pick a topic of current interest and present students with a simplified bill. For example, a House Select Committee on Air Quality

might consider this fictional bill: "HR 3821: Air Pollution Reduction Act—Whereas air pollution is a serious problem, Be it resolved that legislation be enacted to reduce auto emissions by one-third within five years."
- Emphasize the importance of students developing their roles fully and staying in character during the simulation.

PROCEDURE ★★★★★★★★★★★★★★★★

Introduce the Simulation Use Activity Sheet 2A (Background Brief) as the basis for this lesson. Bring a newspaper to class and point out the many references to congressional committees and subcommittees. Review the role that hearings play in committee work.

Prepare for the Simulation Use Activity Sheet 2B (Preparing for the Simulation) as the basis for this lesson. Pay particular attention to Step 3. Focus students' attention on the particular committee and subject they will simulate. Help students choose witnesses to represent both sides of the issue, and assign party affiliations to students so they may prepare questions from their party's perspective. Assign Step 5 as homework. Distribute Activity Sheet 2C (Conducting the Simulation) in advance.

Conduct the Simulation Use Activity Sheets 2C (Conducting the Simulation) and 2E as the basis for this lesson. Arrange desks to simulate a panel for the committee members and a witness table. Guide students through the procedure. You will function as a moderator. Be aware of the time allowed for each witness. Step in as needed to keep the simulation realistic, but strive as much as possible for a hands-off approach.

Review the Simulation Use Activity Sheet 2D (Reviewing the Simulation) as the basis for this lesson. This sheet functions well as a homework activity or as a guide for a classroom discussion.

Government Simulations and Debates

Simulation 2: A Congressional Committee Hearing

⭐ **DIRECTIONS** You will participate in a simulated congressional committee hearing. To help you prepare, read the Background Brief. Then answer the questions.

★ ★ ★ ★ ★ ★ ★ ★ ★ ★ ★ ★ ★ ★ ★ ★ **Background Brief** ★ ★ ★ ★ ★ ★ ★ ★ ★ ★ ★ ★ ★ ★ ★ ★

An old joke says, "Committees keep minutes, but waste hours."

One can also argue that as committees are keeping minutes, they actually *save* time. Committees accomplish in a few weeks what individual legislators would require years of work to complete. Thousands of bills are introduced in Congress during each session. (In one year, nearly 40,000 pieces of legislation might be submitted.) Obviously, no individual Senator or Representative could read, understand, and respond to such a mountain of information. Committees, therefore, initially consider individual bills in various areas, investigate their merits, and make recommendations to the entire House and Senate. The committee system also allows individual lawmakers to become specialists in certain areas.

Congress has four basic kinds of committees: standing committees, select committees, joint committees, and conference committees. All have the power to hold hearings. A committee hearing involves testimony from people interested in the bill. Witnesses typically include experts on the subject of the bill, officials from government agencies that would be affected by the bill, and members of interest groups.

Hearings are critical to committee work. In theory the hearing process informs representatives about the bill under consideration. In reality congressional staff members do most of the research and work on such bills. Hearings are important for other reasons as well. Media coverage gives committee members an opportunity to publicize their accomplishments and helps focus public attention on issues being considered. Individual citizens may also use committee hearings to participate in the legislative process.

★ ★

1. What is a committee hearing? What is the purpose of these hearings?

2. Who are the major participants in committee hearings?

3. Complete this sentence: "It is important to understand how congressional committee hearings function because . . ."

4. What role would you like to play in a simulated committee hearing? Why?

Government Simulations and Debates

Simulation 2: A Congressional Committee Hearing

⭐ **DIRECTIONS** You will participate in a simulated congressional committee hearing. To help you prepare, complete the steps below.

Step 1. **Prepare a Simulation Folder** Use a folder to organize the various papers you will need for your committee hearing simulation. Include any activity sheets your teacher hands out (such as this one), research materials, and notes you take. Update your folder as you proceed.

Step 2. **Understand the Roles in the Simulation** The main players in a committee hearing are the chairperson of the committee, the committee members, and the witnesses. Members of the media are usually present as well. In the space below, briefly describe the role each person plays during a committee hearing.

- Chairperson

- Committee Members

- Witnesses

- Reporters

Step 3. **Choose a Committee and a Bill for it to Consider**

Write your decisions below.

- Committee:

- Bill to Consider:

Step 4. **Decide on Roles** Work with your classmates to agree on the roles that each student will play. Make sure you choose appropriate witness roles. For example, if your committee is holding a hearing on an air pollution bill, witnesses might include representatives of environmental and industry groups.

Step 5. **Research and Rehearse Your Role** If you are a committee member, you should decide which state you represent, your state's interests, your political party, and your party's position. If you are a witness, you should prepare your testimony supporting or opposing the bill, and explaining your reasons. Make sure you take notes to guide you during the simulation.

Government Simulations and Debates

Simulation 2: A Congressional Committee Hearing

DIRECTIONS In this simulation you will experience committee work first hand by simulating a committee hearing. Do so by completing the steps below. Use the space below each step to take notes during the simulation.

Step 1. **Call the Committee to Order** This is the responsibility of the committee chairperson.

Step 2. **Go over the Agenda** The chairperson should also make some brief introductory remarks explaining the purpose of the hearing, and then have someone read the bill to be considered.

Step 3. **Call Witnesses** The chairperson will call witnesses in turn. Each will give a brief speech and then answer questions from committee members.

Step 4. **Hold a Committee Debate and "Markup Session"** Once the testimony and questions have been completed, committee members should briefly debate whether the bill should be killed or reported. Committee members may modify the bill in a "markup session" if they think it would improve the bill.

Step 5. **Vote** The final committee action will be to vote on whether the bill should be killed or reported. After the vote, the chairperson will adjourn the committee.

Government Simulations and Debates

Activity Sheet 2D   **Reviewing the Simulation**

Simulation 2: A Congressional Committee Hearing

DIRECTIONS — Think carefully about your experience in the simulation as you answer the questions below.

The Simulation ★★

1. What was the best part of the simulation? What was the worst part of it? Explain your answers.

_____

_____

2. How well do you think you and your classmates re-created an actual committee hearing?

_____

_____

3. Why is a simulation a good way to learn about how committees and committee hearings function?

_____

_____

Your Role in the Simulation ★★★★★★★★★★★★★★★★★★★★★★★★★★★★★★★★★★★

4. How well do you think you performed your role in the simulation? Could you have done anything

better? Explain your answer. _____

_____

_____

5. Identify the three most important things you learned from participating in this simulation.

- _____
- _____
- _____

6. Write a brief paragraph explaining how this simulation helped you learn more about the U.S.

government. _____

_____

_____

_____

_____

Name _____ Date _____ Class _____

Simulation 2: A Congressional Committee Hearing

★ **DIRECTIONS** Use the stationery to plan the agenda and take notes during your hearing.

THE UNITED STATES CONGRESS
★★★★★★★★★★★★★★★★★★★★★★★
Agenda

Today's Date: _____

Committee Name: _____

Bill to Consider: _____

Agenda Items:

   I. Call to Order

   II. Introduction and Opening Statement By Chairperson

  III. Reading of the Bill

  IV. Opening Statements by Committee Members

   V. Testimony

Witness 1	**Witness 3**
Name: _____	Name: _____
Organization: _____	Organization: _____
Witness 2	**Witness 4**
Name: _____	Name: _____
Organization: _____	Organization: _____

  VI. Committee Discussion and Markup Session

 VII. Committee Vote on Bill

VIII. Adjournment

Government Simulations and Debates

Debate 3: A Line-Item Veto for the President?

"The Washington rules have changed for good," announced President Bill Clinton in 1997, "and for the good of the American people."

The President was talking about his first use—and the first use by any president—of the line-item veto. The line-item veto gives the president the power to veto only certain parts of bills submitted by Congress. Before, the president's only choices were vetoing or signing the bill as a whole. For years many people had been calling on Congress to pass the line-item veto. The Republican Congress finally did so in 1996.

The presidential line-item veto had long been the subject of debate. Proponents had argued that it would give the president the power to control pork-barrel spending. Opponents argued that it would be ineffectual, even unconstitutional. Now that it is law, the debate is more heated than ever.

DIRECTIONS Complete the steps below to learn about both sides of this issue. You will research and debate this resolution:

Resolved: The president of the United States should have the line-item veto.

| Step 1. | **Learn About the Issue** Begin by researching the resolution. Learn about the passage of the line-item veto in 1996 and presidential use of it since then. Consult your textbook, other books, periodical articles, and other appropriate sources. The chart in the front of this book will guide you in your research and serve as a place for you to record what you learn. Your goal is to find or develop on your own at least three arguments for retaining the presidential line-item veto and three arguments against it. As you identify each argument, make sure you take notes of the statistics, quotations, and other evidence that support each argument. Make sure you also develop responses or refutations to the arguments on both sides.

| Step 2. | **Debate the Issue** Once you have completed your research, you are ready to proceed with the debate. Organize two teams: one that will support the resolution, and one that will oppose it. The debate will consist of presentations, questions, and rebuttals. Refer to page vi in the front of this booklet for a description of the debate format.

| Step 3. | **Reflect on the Issue**

DIRECTIONS On a separate sheet of paper, complete the following:

1. Write a paragraph that identifies your opinion about the presidential line-item veto and explains the reasons for your position.

2. Assess the constitutionality of the presidential line-item veto.

3. **Activity:** Consult the *Congressional Record* to find the text of a recent bill. Assuming the role of the president, identify the parts of the bill you would eliminate by using the line-item veto. Explain why you would veto those parts of the bill.

Simulation 3: Teacher Strategy

THE NATIONAL SECURITY COUNCIL

In this simulation students will assume the roles of members of the National Security Council as they consider the United States' response to a foreign crisis.

PURURE ★★★★★★★★★★★★★★★★★

Because the National Security Council (NSC) is so powerful, its activities are carefully followed and analyzed in the media. Understanding how the NSC operates will help students to understand the development of U.S. foreign policy and to read the media reports more thoughtfully.

OBJECTIVES ★★★★★★★★★★★★★★★★

By participating in this simulation, students will:
• identify the major role played by the National Security Council in U.S. foreign policy
• describe the process by which the NSC operates
• analyze the advantages and disadvantages of various foreign policy options

TIME REQUIRED ★★★★★★★★★★★★★

This simulation activity is designed to be conducted over the course of one week (five class periods, plus out-of-class preparation time). You can abbreviate the time required by doing much of the preparatory work yourself. Consider devoting at least two class periods to the simulation.

MATERIALS ★★★★★★★★★★★★★★★★★

• Student copies of Activity Sheets 3A, 3B, 3C, 3D, and 3E
• Folders
• National newspapers
• Newsmagazines

TEACHING TIPS ★★★★★★★★★★★★★★

• This simulation works best with a topic of current interest; students should simulate the NSC considering still unresolved international developments.
• Most NSC meetings include individuals who are not part of the NSC proper. Typically, experts with specialized knowledge are invited to NSC meetings. In the classroom these experts can be used to expand the number of students who participate in the simulation.
• Emphasize the importance of students developing their roles fully, and their staying in character during the simulation. You may wish to have students role play the positions of real officials, by mimicking their dress, mannerisms, and opinions.

PROCEDURE ★★★★★★★★★★★★★★★★

Introduce the Simulation Use Activity Sheet 3A (Background Brief) as the basis for this lesson. Bring newspaper and magazine articles describing evolving international situations to class. Highlight any reports of NSC activities, especially quotations by the president's National Security Advisor. Assign Activity Sheet 3E as homework.

Prepare for the Simulation Use Activity Sheet 3B (Preparing for the Simulation) as the basis for this lesson. Begin by focusing students' attention on the particular international situation they will consider in the simulation. Then guide them through each step. Assign Step 5 as homework. Considering distributing Activity Sheet 3C (Conducting the Simulation) in advance to help students prepare for the simulation.

Conduct the Simulation Use Activity Sheet 3C (Conducting the Simulation) as the basis for this lesson. Make sure that students stay in character. Function as a moderator, keeping students on track and on agenda. Step in as needed to keep the simulation realistic, but strive as much as possible for a hands-off approach.

Review the Simulation Use Activity Sheet 3D (Reviewing the Simulation) for this lesson. This sheet functions well as a homework activity or use it as a guide for a classroom discussion about the simulation.

Government Simulations and Debates

Activity Sheet 3A   **Background Brief**

Simulation 3: The National Security Council

DIRECTIONS You will participate in a simulated meeting of the National Security Council. To help
you prepare, read the Background Brief. Then answer the questions.

★ ★ ★ ★ ★ ★ ★ ★ ★ ★ ★ ★ ★ ★ ★ ★ **Background Brief** ★ ★ ★ ★ ★ ★ ★ ★ ★ ★ ★ ★ ★ ★ ★ ★

The National Security Council (NSC) is arguably the most important office in the
Executive Office of the President. The NSC considers the most urgent matters confronting the government: those concerning the very safety and security of the United States.

Congress created the NSC in the aftermath of World War II to help coordinate U.S.
foreign and military policy. From its inception the NSC was an advisory agency to help
the president make key decisions. The NSC also supervises the Central Intelligence
Agency (CIA). Because of these important responsibilities, and because several
presidents have relied heavily on the NSC, its power and influence have at times
exceeded those of any other government agency.

The president heads the NSC. Other members of the NSC are the vice president, the
secretary of state, the secretary of defense, and the national security advisor, who directs
the NSC's staff. The national security advisor is often a close friend and ally of the president. The president can expand the NSC informally by inviting other government officials
to participate in NSC meetings. For example, the director of the CIA and the chairman of
the Joint Chiefs of Staff are frequent participants in NSC meetings.

NSC meetings are held on an as-needed basis. When an international development
clearly affects, or is likely to affect, U.S. interests, the president may call an NSC meeting
to develop and implement a response to the situation. Experts on particular geographic
areas or foreign governments are often included in the meetings to contribute their specialized knowledge.

An NSC meeting gathers some of the world's most powerful people and foremost
experts, all of whom consider how the U.S. should respond to worldwide developments.
It is no wonder, then, that NSC activities are of keen interest to U.S. citizens.

★ ★

1. What is the purpose of the National Security Council?

2. Assess the importance of the NSC in the U.S. government.

3. Who are the permanent NSC members? What other officials often participate in NSC meetings?

4. Identify at least three international developments or events that the NSC would be likely to consider.

5. What role would you like to play in a simulated NSC meeting? Why?

Government Simulations and Debates

Simulation 3: The National Security Council

⭐ **DIRECTIONS** You will participate in a simulation of a National Security Council (NSC) meeting. To help you prepare, complete the steps below.

Step 1. **Prepare a Simulation Folder** Use a folder to organize the various papers you will need for your simulation. Your folder should include any activity sheets (such as this one) your teacher hands out, research materials, and notes you take. Update your folder as you proceed.

Step 2. **Choose a Topic for the NSC to Consider** Consult current newspaper and other periodical reports to choose an international development for the NSC to consider at the meeting.

Step 3. **Understand the Roles in the Simulation** The participants in NSC meetings are listed below. Next to each, briefly describe the role each person would play in a meeting about the topic you identified in Step 2.

Members of the NSC

- President _____
- Vice President _____
- Secretary of State _____
- Secretary of Defense _____

Frequent Participants in NSC Meetings

- Director of the Central Intelligence Agency _____
- Chairman of the Joint Chiefs of Staff _____
- experts in relevant fields _____

Step 4. **Decide on Roles** Work with your classmates to agree on the roles that each student will play.

Step 5. **Research and Rehearse Your Role** You will present a five to ten minute speech arguing for a particular United States response to the international development you identified in Step 2. Present that response from the perspective of your role in the simulation. (For example, if you are assuming the role of secretary of defense, you will discuss the role of the armed forces.) On a separate sheet of paper, outline your presentation and prepare to make your argument to the president.

Government Simulations and Debates

Simulation 3: The National Security Council

DIRECTIONS In this simulation you will experience the responsibilities and pressures of the National Security Council (NSC) as you simulate a NSC meeting to respond to an international development. Do so by completing the steps below. Use the space below each step to take notes during the simulation.

Step 1. Call the Meeting to Order This is the responsibility of the president.

_____

_____

Step 2. Present the Situation Depending on the international development you are considering, any participant in the meeting may do this. He or she should briefly describe the situation and its implications for the United States.

_____

_____

Step 3. Make Presentations The president will call on each participant to present relevant information from his or her perspective and responsibilities.

_____

_____

Step 4. Discuss the Situation The president will supervise a discussion of the situation. He or she should call on different officials for additional information and implications of the various actions being considered.

_____

_____

Step 5. Decide The president is ultimately responsible for a decision. Once he or she has decided, appropriate officials should be directed to take particular actions. In response, each official should detail how these orders are to be carried out.

_____

_____

Step 6. Adjourn the Meeting This is the responsibility of the president.

_____

_____

Government Simulations and Debates

Activity Sheet 3D   **Reviewing the Simulation**

Simulation 3: The National Security Council

DIRECTIONS To help you get the most from the simulation, think carefully about your experience in it as you answer the questions below.

The Simulation ★★★

1. What was the best thing about the simulation? What was the worse thing about it? Explain your answers. _____

_____

_____

_____

2. Evaluate the realism of your simulation. In other words, how well do you think you and your classmates recreated the workings of an actual NSC meeting? _____

_____

_____

3. Compare the actions implemented by your simulated NSC to those taken by the actual NSC.

_____

_____

Your Role in the Simulation ★★

4. How well do you think you performed your role in the simulation? Could you have done anything better? Explain your answer. _____

_____

_____

5. Identify the three most important things you learned from participating in this simulation.

• _____

• _____

• _____

6. Write a brief paragraph that explains how this simulation helped you learn more about the U.S. government. _____

_____

_____

_____

_____

Government Simulations and Debates

Activity Sheet 3E

Simulation 3: The National Security Council

⭐ **DIRECTIONS** Complete the chart to help you understand the structure of the NSC.

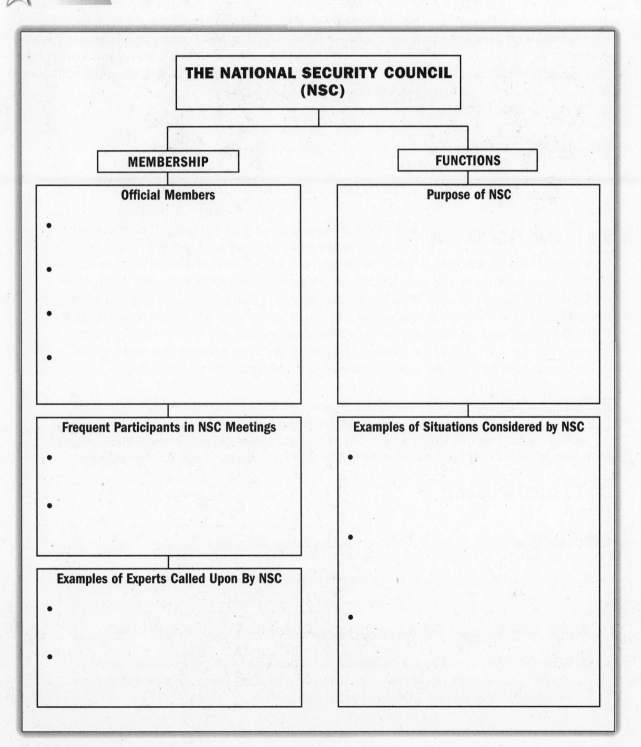

THE NATIONAL SECURITY COUNCIL (NSC)

MEMBERSHIP

Official Members
-
-
-
-

Frequent Participants in NSC Meetings
-
-

Examples of Experts Called Upon By NSC
-
-

FUNCTIONS

Purpose of NSC

Examples of Situations Considered by NSC
-
-
-

Government Simulations and Debates

Debate 4: Judicial Activism versus Judicial Restraint

The judicial branch was created to settle disputes. But what happens when there is a dispute about the judicial branch itself? This problem has confronted the United States for decades and continues to do so today.

The debate is over judicial activism versus judicial restraint. An ongoing subject in the pages of newspapers and magazines, over the airwaves, and even in the courts themselves, defining the proper role of the judiciary is debated by government scholars, officials, and ultimately, the public. Proponents of judicial activism argue that it is necessary in a rapidly changing country. Those who support judicial restraint see judicial activism as unconstitutional and undemocratic.

DIRECTIONS Complete the steps below to learn about both sides of this issue. You will research and debate this resolution:

Resolved: Judicial activism is superior to judicial restraint.

Step 1. **Learn About the Issue** Begin by defining *judicial activism* and *judicial restraint*. Work with your teacher and other students to reach a consensus on the definitions. Once the terms of the debate have been defined, you are ready to research the resolution. Consult your textbook, other books, periodical articles, and other appropriate sources. The chart in the front of this book will guide you in your research, and help you organize and record what you learn. Your goal is to find or develop on your own at least three arguments for judicial activism and three arguments for judicial restraint. As you identify each argument, make sure you take notes of the statistics, quotations, and other evidence that support each argument. Make sure you also develop refutations to the arguments on both sides.

Step 2. **Debate the Issue** Once you have completed your research, you are ready to proceed with the debate. Organize two teams: a team that will support judicial activism and a team that will oppose it. The debate will consist of presentations, questions, and rebuttals. Refer to page vi in the front of this booklet for a description of the debate format.

Step 3. **Reflect on the Issue**

DIRECTIONS On a separate sheet of paper complete the following:

1. Write a paragraph that identifies your opinion about judicial activism and explains the reasons for your position.

2. Why was it important to begin the debate by defining the terms of the resolution?

3. **Activity:** Locate a news report on a recent court decision. Copy or cut out the article. Attach the article to a report you write about the ruling, explaining why the ruling is an example of either judicial activism or judicial restraint.

Simulation 4: Teacher Strategy

TINKER V. *DES MOINES INDEPENDENT COMMUNITY SCHOOL DISTRICT*

In this simulation students will act as justices, attorneys, and friends of the court as they consider the case of *Tinker* v. *Des Moines Independent Community School District*.

PURPOSE ★★★★★★★★★★★★★★★★★

The Supreme Court, through its landmark decisions, has had a fundamental effect on life in the United States. Understanding the process through which the Court reaches its decisions is, therefore, critical to student understanding of U.S. government. Because the *Tinker* case involved high school students and their activities at school, it is very well suited for student simulation.

OBJECTIVES ★★★★★★★★★★★★★★★

- to identify the significance of a landmark Supreme Court ruling
- to describe the process through which the Supreme Court considers cases and renders opinions
- to analyze the role of the Supreme Court in deciding issues of free speech

TIME REQUIRED ★★★★★★★★★★★★★

This simulation activity is designed to be conducted over the course of one week (five class periods in conjunction with studying the judicial branch). You can abbreviate the time, but consider devoting at least two class periods to the simulation to allow adequate preparation, participation, and evaluation time.

MATERIALS ★★★★★★★★★★★★★★★★

- Student copies of Activity Sheets 4A, 4B, 4C, 4D, and 4E
- Folders
- Costumes, if desired. Attorneys, for example, can wear dress clothes; justices can wear robes.

TEACHING TIPS ★★★★★★★★★★★★★

- Emphasize the importance of students developing their roles fully and staying in character. Advanced students can use records of the actual Supreme Court session to develop their briefs and questions.

- Encourage students playing the roles of justices to thoughtfully challenge the arguments of students playing the roles of the attorneys.
- Assign one student to time presentations and enforce the time limits.

PROCEDURE ★★★★★★★★★★★★★★★★

Introduce the Simulation Use Activity Sheet 4A (Background Brief) as the basis for this lesson. Emphasize the volatility of this period and guide students as they compare and contrast student freedoms in the mid-1960s with student freedoms today.

Prepare for the Simulation Use Activity Sheet 4B (Preparing for the Simulation) as the basis for this lesson. Focus students' attention on the basic questions of the case (Step 2). They should carefully consider these questions and respond thoughtfully to the implications. Consider distributing Activity Sheet 4C (Conducting the Simulation) in advance to help students prepare for the simulation.

Conduct the Simulation Use Activity Sheet 4C (Conducting the Simulation) as the basis for this lesson. Students should carefully adhere to the steps, which are closely modeled on actual Supreme Court procedures.

Review the Simulation Use Activity Sheets 4D (Reviewing the Simulation) and 4E as the basis for this lesson. These sheets function well as homework activities, or you can use them as guides for classroom discussion about the simulation and the case itself. You may also choose to evaluate individual student work on the other activity sheets.

Government Simulations and Debates

Simulation 4: *Tinker* v. *Des Moines Independent Community School District*

⭐ **DIRECTIONS** You will participate in a simulation of a Supreme Court case. To help you prepare, read the Background Brief. Then answer the questions.

★ ★ ★ ★ ★ ★ ★ ★ ★ ★ ★ ★ ★ ★ ★ ★ ★ **Background Brief** ★ ★ ★ ★ ★ ★ ★ ★ ★ ★ ★ ★ ★ ★ ★ ★ ★

It is 1965. In Southeast Asia, Communist North Vietnam, aided by Communist rebels in South Vietnam, is fighting to conquer non-Communist South Vietnam. The United States, staunchly opposed to Communist expansion, has been helping the South Vietnamese government. In 1965 the United States increases its aid and for the first time commits ground troops to the conflict.

Already deeply divided about the U.S. role in the conflict, Americans engage in heated debate about the war, sparking protest marches and dinner table conflicts in every community—and in many schools.

In Des Moines, Iowa, high school students Mary Beth Tinker, 13, and her brother John, 15, have strong feelings about the war that they and other students plan to express by wearing black armbands to school. The armbands symbolize mourning for U.S. soldiers who are dying in the war.

When the Des Moines school board finds out about the students' plans, they worry that the armbands will bring the passions of the war debate into the classroom, disrupting everyone's education. They decide to prohibit the armbands. Anyone who wears them will be suspended.

The Tinkers and the other students wear their armbands to school anyway. The school board makes good on its promise, and immediately suspends five students. The Tinkers take what they have learned about the U.S. government to heart—they take the school district to court.

In the suit the Tinkers' parents argue that the school board has violated the students' First Amendment rights to free speech. They point out that other, similar symbols, such as campaign buttons, are allowed in school. The school board counters by arguing that the armbands would be disruptive, and might even lead to fights. After losing their case in two lower courts, the Tinkers appeal to the United States Supreme Court. By 1969 the number of U.S. troops in Vietnam has increased nine times, and the war continues to divide the country. The nation anxiously awaits the Court's decision.

★ ★

1. Identify the main issues in the case of *Tinker* v. *Des Moines Independent Community School District*.

2. You will simulate this Supreme Court case in class. What role would you like to play? Why?

Government Simulations and Debates

Activity Sheet 4B   **Preparing for the Simulation**

Simulation 4: *Tinker* v. *Des Moines Independent Community School District*

⭐ **DIRECTIONS** In this simulation you will act out the roles of Supreme Court justices and others involved in the landmark case, *Tinker* v. *Des Moines Independent Community School District*. To prepare for the simulation, complete the steps below.

| **Step 1.** | **Prepare a Simulation Folder** Use a folder to organize the various papers you will need for your simulation. Your folder should include any activity sheets (such as this one) your teacher hands out, research materials, and notes you take. Update your folder as you proceed.

| **Step 2.** | **Consider the Questions of the Case** The Supreme Court agreed to hear the *Tinker* case because it raised two important questions. These questions are listed below. Carefully consider each one, and record your thoughts.

• Is wearing an armband a form of free speech?

• How far does the right of free speech extend to students?

| **Step 3.** | **Understand the Roles in the Simulation** The main participants in a Supreme Court session are listed below. Briefly describe the role each person plays during a Supreme Court session.

• Chief Justice

• Associate Justices

• Attorneys

• Friends of the Court

| **Step 4.** | **Decide on Roles** Determine which student will play each role in the simulation and decide on appropriate costumes if you are using them.

| **Step 5.** | **Research and Rehearse Your Role** Attorneys will be given 10 minutes to present their briefs to the Court and should be prepared to answer questions from the justices. Justices should prepare questions they plan to ask each attorney. Friends of the court should prepare amicus curiae (friend of the court) briefs that can be presented to the Court within the five minutes allowed.

Government Simulations and Debates

Activity Sheet 4C   Conducting the Simulation

Simulation 4: *Tinker v. Des Moines Independent Community School District*

⭐ **DIRECTIONS** — You will conduct a simulation of a Supreme Court session. Follow the steps below.

Step 1. Call to Order The chief justice should call the session to order and identify the case the Court will consider.

Step 2. The Court Hears Briefs The lawyer for the plaintiffs (the Tinkers) should read the brief supporting the Tinkers to the Court. Those who have prepared amicus curie briefs on behalf of the Tinkers should then read them. Next, the lawyer for the respondents (the Des Moines Independent Community School District) should read the brief supporting the school district, followed by those who have prepared amicus curie briefs on the district's behalf.

Step 3. The Court Hears Oral Arguments From the Plaintiffs The lawyer for the plaintiff should present a prepared oral argument. During the presentation any one of the justices may interrupt with questions asking for more information or challenges to the argument, to which the lawyer must respond.

Step 4. The Court Hears Oral Arguments From the Respondent The lawyer for the respondent should present a prepared oral argument. During the presentation any one of the justices may interrupt with questions asking for more information or challenges to the argument, to which the lawyer must respond.

Step 5. The Court Holds Conference After the arguments have been heard, the chief justice will adjourn the session, and the justices will retire to a conference. By tradition, each justice will shake hands with the other eight before they consider the case. The chief justice will then summarize the case, make his or her recommendation, and open the debate.

Step 6. The Court Issues its Opinions Depending on how the case is decided, the justices will then draft a unanimous opinion, a majority opinion, concurring opinions, or dissenting opinions. The Court then announces its decision, and presents its opinion(s) to the class.

Government Simulations and Debates

Simulation 4: *Tinker v. Des Moines Independent Community School District*

⭐ **DIRECTIONS** To help you get the most from the simulation, think carefully about your experience in the simulation as you answer the questions below.

The Simulation ★★★★★★★★★★★★★★★★★★★★★★★★★★★★★★★★★★★★★

1. What was the best thing about the simulation? What was the worse thing about it? Explain.

_____

2. How well do you think you and your classmates re-created the workings of an actual Supreme Court

session? _____

3. How did the Supreme Court rule in the *Tinker* case? _____

4. In its opinion, the Court declared that "It can hardly be argued that students shed their constitutional rights to freedom of speech or expression at the schoolhouse gate. . . . Students in school as well as out of school are persons under our Constitution." Explain what this statement means. Why is the distinction between freedom of "speech" and freedom of "expression" important in this case?

_____

5. How can you see the results of the *Tinker* decision in your school today? _____

_____

6. How might the *Tinker* ruling affect you personally? _____

_____

Your Role in the Simulation ★★★★★★★★★★★★★★★★★★★★★★★★★★★★★★★★

7. What was the most difficult part of the simulation? Explain. _____

_____

8. How well do you think you performed your role in the simulation? Could you have done anything

better? Explain your answer. _____

_____

9. Identify the three most important things learned from participating in this simulation.

- _____

- _____

- _____

10. On a separate sheet of paper, write a brief paragraph explaining how this simulation helped you learn more about the Supreme Court at work.

Name _____ Date _____ Class _____

Activity Sheet 4E

Simulation 4: *Tinker* v. *Des Moines Independent Community School District*

RESPONDING TO A HISTORICAL EVENT

⭐ **DIRECTIONS** Use your research and the experience you had in the simulation to answer the following questions.

1. The *Tinker* case was widely publicized during the mid-1960.s. Research to find editorials written about the case from newspapers or news magazines from that period. Read letters to the editor about the case. How would you characterize public response to the case? Support your opinion with evidence from your research. _____

_____

_____

_____

_____

_____

_____

_____

_____

_____

2. What is your impression of the armbands worn by the students? Do you find them offensive? Harmless? Something else? Explain your opinion, considering the historical context in which the armbands were worn. _____

_____

_____

_____

3. Explain how opponents of the Tinkers' beliefs would benefit from the Tinkers' actions. _____

_____

_____

_____

Name _____ Date _____ Class _____

Debate 5: Restrictions on Immigration?

As a nation, the United States has received more immigrants from more places than any other country in the world. The heritage of providing a haven for those fleeing terrible hardships in their homelands has been a proud tradition.

Many citizens today, however, see immigration as a problem. They say that the United States does not have adequate resources to share with the hundreds of thousands of immigrants that come to the U.S. each year. They want further restrictions on immigration. Other U.S. citizens think we should maintain or expand the current immigration quotas.

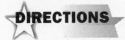 **DIRECTIONS** Complete the steps below to learn about both sides of this issue. You will research and debate this resolution:

Resolved: Immigration to the United States should be further restricted.

Step 1. **Learn About the Issue** Begin by researching the resolution to learn more about immigration. What are the current immigration quotas? What is the rationale behind these limits? Consult your textbook, other books, periodical articles, and other appropriate sources. Then develop at least three arguments for further restricting immigration and three arguments against such restrictions. As you identify each argument, make sure you take notes of the statistics, quotations, and other evidence that support each argument. Make sure you also develop responses or refutations to the arguments on both sides.

Step 2. **Debate the Issue** Once you have completed your research, proceed with the debate. Organize two teams: a team that will support the resolution and a team that will oppose it. The debate will consist of presentations, questions, and rebuttals. Refer to page iv in the front of this booklet for a description of the debate format.

Step 3. **Reflect on the Issue**

DIRECTIONS On a separate sheet of paper complete the following:

1. Write a paragraph that identifies your opinion about the resolution and explain the reasons for your position.

2. Franklin Delano Roosevelt said, "All of our people all over the country . . . are immigrants or descendants of immigrants, including even those who came over here on the *Mayflower*." In a paragraph, explain why FDR was correct.

3. **Activity:** Write a letter to a senator or a representative requesting his or her position paper on immigration limits. Ask for specific information, including voting records and positions on any relevant, pending legislation. Compare their responses to your answer to the first question.

Simulation 5: Teacher Strategy

MOCK POLICE STOPS

In this simulation, students will assume the roles of police and citizens as they simulate police stops.

PURPOSE ★★★★★★★★★★★★★★★★★★★

The interaction of police and citizens in the United States has precipitated major events from landmark Supreme Court decisions to riots. Popular entertainment reflects the culture's fascination with law enforcement. The enforcement power of government is most directly felt through this interaction. By simulating police stops, students will more fully understand government-citizen interaction.

OBJECTIVES ★★★★★★★★★★★★★★★★

By participating in this simulation, students will:
- develop an appreciation of their rights as citizens
- develop an appreciation of the challenges faced by law enforcement officials
- investigate the inherent dilemma of protecting individual rights while protecting public safety

TIME REQUIRED ★★★★★★★★★★★★★★

This simulation is designed to be conducted over one week (five class periods, plus out-of-class preparation time), in conjunction with students' studying citizenship and equal justice. You can abbreviate the time required by doing much of the preparatory work yourself. Consider devoting at least two class periods to the simulation.

MATERIALS ★★★★★★★★★★★★★★★★★

- Student copies of Activity Sheets 5A, 5B, 5C, 5D, and 5E
- Folders

TEACHING TIPS ★★★★★★★★★★★★★

- Ensure that police stop scenarios that students develop are appropriate for the classroom.
- Encourage students to develop a wide variety of scenarios, perhaps including the re-creation of an actual, media-reported event. Help them choose scenarios in which civil rights and the exclusionary rule are important.
- Emphasize the analysis of each simulation as the critical learning phase, when students evaluate each scenario in terms of civil rights issues.

PROCEDURE ★★★★★★★★★★★★★★★★★

Introduce the Simulation Use Activity Sheet 5A (Background Brief) as the basis for this lesson. Lead a class discussion about high-profile police stops that have wider consequences, and focus students' attention on the difficult dilemma of protecting rights while protecting public safety.

Prepare for the Simulation Use Activity Sheet 5B (Preparing for the Simulation) as the basis for this lesson. This activity works well with groups of three to five students, developing scenarios independently. Focus students' attention on the development of the scenarios (each should be realistic, interesting, and involve larger civil rights or constitutional questions), the scripts (each should provide general character guidelines and a rough "plot" for the scenario) and the lists (each should guide students as they act out the scenarios). Consider distributing Activity Sheet 5C (Conducting the Simulation) in advance to help students prepare.

Conduct the Simulation Use Activity Sheet 5C (Conducting the Simulation) as the basis for this lesson. Step in as needed to keep the simulations realistic and appropriate for the classroom, but strive as much as possible for a hands-off approach.

Review the Simulation Use Activity Sheets 5D (Reviewing the Simulation) and 5E as the basis for this lesson. The sheets function well as homework activities, or you can use them as guides for a classroom discussion about the simulation.

Government Simulations and Debates

Simulation 5: Mock Police Stops

⭐ **DIRECTIONS** You will participate in a simulated police stop to help you understand government-citizen interaction. To help you prepare, read the Background Brief. Then answer the questions.

★ ★ ★ ★ ★ ★ ★ ★ ★ ★ ★ ★ ★ ★ ★ ★ ★ ★ | **Background Brief** | ★ ★ ★ ★ ★ ★ ★ ★ ★ ★ ★ ★ ★ ★ ★ ★ ★

It is a situation familiar to most U.S. citizens. They see it on television news, and re-created in entertainment programs. They see it in person, daily, as they drive to work or social engagements. Many have experienced it themselves. Most know someone who has had the experience.

It is the police stop—when law enforcement officers, usually members of a local police force, light up a motorist's rear-view mirror with red or blue flashing lights that mean just one thing: pull over, now.

Most police stops end with issuing a ticket or a warning, but the possibility of important legal repercussions is never far from the participants' minds. Police officers are keenly aware of the potential dangers involved in stopping strangers. They know, too, that they have a solemn duty to respect the rights of the individuals they stop, at the same time they are protecting public safety. Citizens stopped by the police find their emotions running high and are anxious that they be treated well and that their rights be protected.

The events of the police stop are the most dramatic and concrete instances of the interaction between the enforcement authority of the government and the citizenry. These events can have dramatic and unforeseen consequences. Bungled stops have even led to riots, as people protest the perceived police violations of civil rights. Mistakes made by officers during stops have resulted in criminals going free. Conversely, police officers have been injured or even killed in routine traffic stops. Civil rights issues raised during police stops have led to court rulings and legislation that have fundamentally changed the way citizens interact with their government.

The police stop, common as it is, is an event colored by fundamental issues of government, law, and civil rights. A police stop represents a delicate balance. On one end of the scale, police officers have the duty to protect the public's safety. On the other hand, they have the duty to respect individual rights. Occasionally, what starts out as a routine traffic stop escalates into a more serious situation involving other kinds of criminal activities. What hangs in the balance during a police stop is the ideals on which the United States was founded.

★ ★

1. Explain the last sentence of the Background Brief.

2. Why do you think police shows and movies about law enforcement are so popular?

3. Like elected officials, police officers need certain personal characteristics. What personal qualities do you think a good police officer should have?

Name _____ Date _____ Class _____

Simulation 5: Mock Police Stops

DIRECTIONS — You will participate in simulations of police stops. To help you prepare, complete the steps below.

Step 1. **Prepare a Simulation Folder** Use a folder to organize the various papers you will need for your simulations. Your folder should include any activity sheets (such as this one) your teacher hands out, research materials, and notes you take. Update your folder as you proceed. _____

_____ ,

_____

Step 2. **Create a Variety of Scenarios** Your task in this step is to develop at least three police-stop scenarios for your group to simulate. Decide who is in the car, the reason the car was stopped by the police, and the basic facts of the situation that will determine the interaction of officers and citizens. For example, a pair of officers might stop a car full of teenagers. What reason did the police have for stopping the car? Perhaps one of the passengers is disrespectful to the officers. How will the police respond? Be creative and specific. Strive to develop scenarios that are interesting, varied, and, most important, involve fundamental questions of civil rights. _____

_____

Step 3. **Develop Scripts** You should develop a script for each police stop scenario. However, your scripts should not specify the exact words that each character will speak. Rather, they should provide general guidelines about the scenario, the events that take place as it develops, and descriptions of the characters and their attitudes and actions.

_____

_____

Step 4. **Assign Roles** Determine which students will play each role in the simulation.

_____

_____

Step 5. **Research and Rehearse Your Role** Students playing the roles of police should develop lists of proper actions during police stops. The lists should include specific "dos" and "do nots" for officers to follow. For example, if an officer is to make an arrest for something other than a traffic ticket, a "do" would be to read the suspect his or her Miranda rights. Students playing motorists and passengers should develop similar lists that identify their rights in each situation. You should adhere to these lists during the simulation.

Government Simulations and Debates

Activity Sheet 5C   Conducting the Simulation

Simulation 5: Mock Police Stops

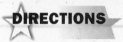 **DIRECTIONS** In this simulation you will experience citizen-government interaction by simulating a police stop. Do so by completing the steps below. Use the space below each step to take notes during the simulation.

Step 1. **Introduce the Scenario** Explain to your classmates any background information to the police stop that you cannot enact. _____

_____

_____

_____

Step 2. **Enact the Scenario** Arrange the classroom appropriately (for example, desks can be arranged to simulate the seats in the stopped car), then proceed with the scenario. Stay in character, and closely follow your scripts and lists. Play the scenario out to a final, logical conclusion. _____

_____

_____

_____

Step 3. **Evaluate the Scenario** Participants in the simulation, as well as the observers should analyze the events of the scenario in the following terms, and in the following order:

- **Civil Liberties** What civil liberties were involved? How were they protected? Were any violated?

- **Constitutional Rights** What Fourth Amendment issues were involved? How were they addressed by the police officers and the citizens?

- **Exclusionary Rule** Was there anything in the stop that would raise this issue later? How would the court rule on it?

- **Supreme Court Decisions** Did the landmark Supreme Court decisions in *Miranda* v. *Arizona* or *Mapp* v. *Ohio* come into play? In what way?

- **Right To Privacy** Was this issue raised? In what way?

- **Right To Safety** How was this right of both the officers and the citizens addressed?

- **Balance** Was there a fair balance between the rights and responsibilities of the police and the rights and responsibilities of the citizens?

Government Simulations and Debates

Simulation 5: Mock Police Stops

⭐ **DIRECTIONS** To help you get the most out of the simulation, think carefully about your experience in the simulation as you answer the questions below.

The Simulation ★

1. What was the best thing about the simulation? What was the worse thing about it? Explain your

answers. _____

_____

_____

2. Evaluate the realism of your simulation. In other words, how well do you think you and your classmates

re-created the events of actual police stops? _____

_____

_____

3. Write a paragraph that answers and explores this question: How do police officers face and resolve

dilemmas in every police stop? _____

_____

_____

Your Role in the Simulation ★

4. How well do you think you performed your role in the simulation? Could you have done anything

better? Explain your answer. _____

_____

_____

5. Identify the three most important things you learned from participating in this simulation. _____

• _____

• _____

• _____

6. Write a brief paragraph that explains how this simulation helped you learn more about the U.S.

government. _____

_____

_____

Name _____ Date _____ Class _____

Simulation 5: Mock Police Stops

⭐ **DIRECTIONS** Complete the chart below to highlight the rights and responsibilities of all parties involved during a police stop.

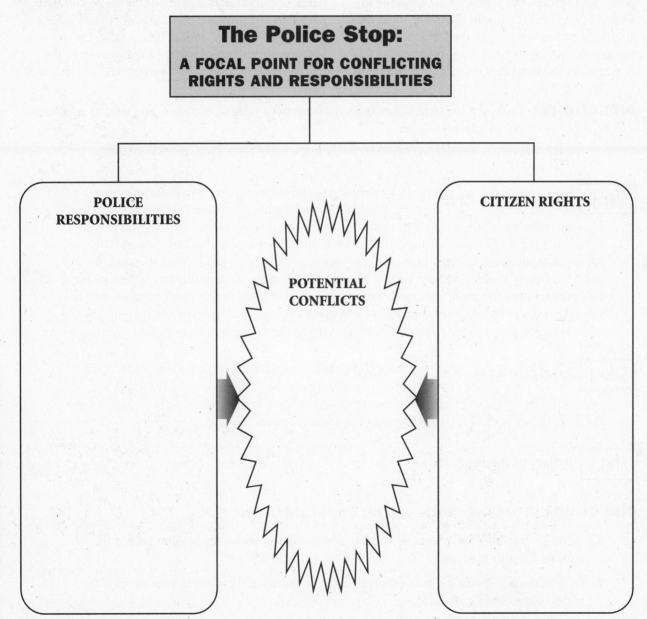

The Police Stop:
A FOCAL POINT FOR CONFLICTING RIGHTS AND RESPONSIBILITIES

POLICE RESPONSIBILITIES

POTENTIAL CONFLICTS

CITIZEN RIGHTS

Government Simulations and Debates

Debate 6: Two-Party versus Multiparty Systems?

Two major political parties already existed by the time George Washington left office. Political parties have become so much a part of the American political landscape that it is nearly impossible to imagine government without them. For more than a century, two major parties, the Democrats and the Republicans, have been dominant.

Although the two-party system has served Americans well, it has its drawbacks. In recent years, many Americans have wanted the political process to be more open to the participation of other political parties, but additional parties have had limited success. Still many Americans believe a multiparty system is more democratic. Do the advantages of a multiparty system outweigh the advantages of a two-party system?

DIRECTIONS Complete the steps below to learn about both sides of this issue. You will research and debate this resolution:

Resolved: A multiparty system is superior to a two-party system.

Step 1. **Learn About the Issue** Begin by defining the terms *multiparty system* and *two-party system*. Work with your teacher and other students to reach a consensus on their definitions. Once the terms of the debate have been defined, you are ready to research the resolution. Consult your textbook, other books, periodical articles, and other appropriate sources. The chart in the front of this book will guide you in your research. Your goal is to find or develop on your own at least three arguments for a multiparty system or for a two-party system and three arguments against it. As you identify each argument, make sure you take notes of the statistics, quotations, and other evidence that supports each argument. Make sure you also develop responses or refutations to the arguments on both sides.

Step 2. **Debate the Issue** Once you have completed your research, organize two teams: a supporting team that will support the resolution, and a team that will oppose it. The debate will consist of presentations, questions, and rebuttals. Refer to page iv in the front of this booklet for a description of the debate format.

Step 3. **Reflect on the Issue**

DIRECTIONS On a separate sheet of paper complete the following:

1. Write a paragraph that identifies your personal opinion about the resolution and the reasons for your position.

2. Do you think it is possible for a powerful third or fourth party to develop in the United States today? Why or why not?

3. **Activity**: Identify a third political party that currently exists. Contact its representatives and request a copy of its platform. Compare and contrast it with the platforms of the two major parties and evaluate the chances for the third party's success.

Simulation 6: Teacher Strategy

AN INTEREST GROUP

In this simulation, students will conceive and create an interest group and create a plan for it to influence government policy and public opinion on its behalf.

PURPOSE ★★★★★★★★★★★★★★★★★★★

Interest groups are major players—if not *the* major players—in the American political game. Their activities are often the fundamental force shaping legislation and, sometimes, public opinion. Since they exert such a powerful influence over the public and its government, students need to develop a firm understanding of their purposes, activities, and power.

OBJECTIVES ★★★★★★★★★★★★★★★★

By participating in this simulation, students will:
- identify the importance of interest group activities
- analyze the processes through which interest groups influence the government and public opinion
- evaluate the role of interest groups in the United States today

TIME REQUIRED ★★★★★★★★★★★★★★

This simulation activity is designed to be conducted over the course of one week (five class periods, plus out-of-class preparations time), in conjunction with student reading and studying about interest groups. You can abbreviate the time required by doing much of the preparatory work yourself. Consider devoting at least two class periods to the simulation itself to allow adequate preparation, participation, and evaluation time.

MATERIALS ★★★★★★★★★★★★★★★★★★

- Student copies of Activity Sheets 6A, 6B, 6C, 6D, and 6E
- Folders
- Outside research materials (optional, if emulating an actual interest group)

TEACHING TIPS ★★★★★★★★★★★★★

- Guide students into identifying appropriate policy areas for their interest groups to operate within. You may direct students to create a miniature group that is concerned with a local or even a school

issue, or you may decide to have them consider topics of national or international concerns.
- An effective technique is to assign to groups of students the tasks of simulating rival interest groups. Each group can then present its plan, and you and the class can evaluate their relative effectiveness.
- Encourage students to tie their simulation to actual events. Consider having students emulate an actual interest group.
- If it seems reasonable, encourage students to extend their simulation by making appropriate contacts outside the classroom. For example, they might organize a presentation to a local governmental body.

PROCEDURE ★★★★★★★★★★★★★★★★★

Introduce the Simulation Use Activity Sheet 6A (Background Brief) as the basis for this lesson. Emphasize the primary role that interest groups play in the United States political and governmental scenes.

Prepare for the Simulation Use Activity Sheets 6B (Preparing for the Simulation) and 6E as the basis for this lesson. Decide whether students will coordinate to simulate a single interest group or whether they will compete as rival interest groups. Students should profile their interest group on Activity Sheet 6E as they proceed. Consider distributing Activity Sheet 6C (Conducting the Simulation) in advance to help students prepare for the simulation.

Conduct the Simulation Use Activity Sheets 6C (Conducting the Simulation) and 6E as the basis for this lesson. Emphasize the presentation and the evaluation of it as the final outcomes of the activity.

Review the Simulation Use Activity Sheet 6D (Reviewing the Simulation) as the basis for this lesson. The sheet functions well as a homework activity, or you can use it as a guide for classroom discussion about the simulation and interest groups generally. You may also choose to evaluate individual student work on the other activity sheets.

Government Simulations and Debates

Activity Sheet 6A

Background Brief

Simulation 6: An Interest Group

⭐ **DIRECTIONS** You will participate in a simulation of an interest group. To help you prepare, read the Background Brief. Then answer the questions.

★ ★ ★ ★ ★ ★ ★ ★ ★ ★ ★ ★ ★ ★ ★ ★ **Background Brief** ★ ★ ★ ★ ★ ★ ★ ★ ★ ★ ★ ★ ★ ★ ★ ★

Interest groups attempt to influence the government on their own behalf. In fact, many have argued that interest groups are the single most powerful force in government and politics, more so, even, than voters, government agencies, and elected officials themselves.

What makes them so powerful? Interest groups can be large, well-funded, and well-organized. Government officials pay special attention to interest groups because they may represent large groups of voters and therefore are expert in shaping public opinion. Often, their leaders are former officials who hold sway with colleagues still in government.

The "average American" *is* represented by interest groups, whether or not he or she wants to be. Virtually every citizen in the United States can find at least one group that is working in his or her interests. Literally thousands of interest groups operate at the local, state, and national levels. No elected official in the United States escapes the influence of interest groups.

Interest groups seek to influence the government in two basic ways. Directly, they contact government officials through lobbyists, who provide important, though often biased, information to officials, present petitions on behalf of what they see as beneficial legislation, and generally try to sway the opinions of officials. During elections, interest groups also often give or withhold support, based on how well the official in question has responded to the interest groups' concerns. These methods and others—especially the distribution of PAC money—give interest groups tremendous influence. Indirectly the groups work to shape public opinion through advertisements, public information campaigns, and other activities. In doing so, they increase their power and influence, especially during elections.

Interest groups often have conflicting interests. Environmental groups, for example, are often at odds with industry groups. Each tries its best to shape government policy and public opinion to its benefit. The battle for influence and support is hard fought, and the stakes are high. The basic constitutional rights of assembly and speech are made concrete in the interest groups.

★ ★

1. Explain the statement: "The 'average American' *is* represented by interest groups, whether or not he or she wants to be."

2. Do you think interest groups wield too much power? Explain.

3. Would it be possible for interest groups to *not* exist, given our Constitution? Explain.

4. Identify the *direct* and *indirect* ways that interest groups seek to influence government.

5. List at least three possibilities for interest groups you would like your simulation group to represent.

Government Simulations and Debates

Activity Sheet 6B   Preparing for the Simulation

Simulation 6: An Interest Group

⭐ **DIRECTIONS** ➤ You will participate in the simulation of an interest group. To prepare for the simulation, complete the steps below.

Step 1. **Prepare a Simulation Folder** Use a folder to organize the various papers you will need for your simulation. Your folder should include any activity sheets (such as this one) your teacher hands out, research materials, and notes you take. Update your folder as you proceed.

Step 2. **Form a Group** Meet with your classmates to organize groups of four or five students each.

Step 3. **Choose an Area of Concern** There are thousands of interest groups concerned with thousands of areas of public policy. You can choose any one you would like. As you make your decision, consider such factors as your group's personal concerns about issues, timeliness, and availability of research materials. Record your decision below.

Step 4. **Choose a Type of Interest Group** Major types of interest groups include business groups, labor groups, agricultural groups, professional associations, environmental interest groups, public interest groups, and single interest groups. As you take your group's area of concern into account, decide which type of interest group you would like to simulate. Record your decision below.

Step 5. **Profile Your Interest Group** Complete the interest group profile on Activity Sheet 6E. Pay particular attention to the *objectives* and *strategies* of your interest group. Your objectives should be specific and your methods of achieving these objectives, through influencing government policy and influencing public opinion, should be even more specific.

Step 6. **Decide on Roles** Since interest groups perform many functions, there are many roles to play. Prominent ones are listed below. For each, identify the main responsibilities and the student who will assume them during the simulation. Add roles as appropriate.

- Leaders _____
- Lobbyists _____
- PAC members _____
- Pollsters _____
- Public Relations Professionals _____

Government Simulations and Debates

Simulation 6: An Interest Group

DIRECTIONS In this simulation you will experience the work of interest groups firsthand. Do so by completing the steps below. Use the space below each step to take notes during the simulation.

Step 1. Conceive a Plan of Action Using your completed Activity Sheets 6B and 6E, create a plan of action. Your plan of action is the course your group will follow to implement the strategies to achieve your objectives. Assign specific tasks to students playing the various roles. For example, the public relations professionals might plan an ad campaign to convince the public to support your objectives. Lobbyists might create briefs for elected officials to convince them of your position. The leadership should coordinate these activities so that they work in harmony toward your objectives.

Step 2. Complete the Necessary Tasks Individuals should complete their tasks individually or in coordination with other appropriate officials. Once they have been completed, the entire group should meet to prepare a presentation of the final, coordinated plan.

Step 3. Present Your Plan Give the prepared presentation to your teacher and classmates.

Step 4. Evaluate Your Plan Answer each of the questions to evaluate the effectiveness of your plan.

- How well were the goals and objectives of the interest group defined?

- How well did the strategies relate to the objectives of the interest group?

- How effective do you judge the strategies for influencing government policy to be? What could make them more effective?

- How effective do you judge the strategies for influencing public opinion to be? What could make them more effective?

- How well did the two types of strategies complement each other?

Step 5. Modify and Implement Your Plan Modify your plan based on the responses given in Step 4. Then, if possible, put your plan into action.

Government Simulations and Debates

Simulation 6: An Interest Group

⭐ **DIRECTIONS** To help you get the most from the simulation, think carefully about your experience in the simulation as you answer the questions below.

The Simulation ★★

1. What was the best thing about the simulation? What was the worse thing about it? Explain your answers.

_____

_____

2. Evaluate the realism of your simulation. In other words, how well do you think you and your classmates recreated the workings of an actual interest group? _____

_____

3. Explain why developing strategies for both influencing government policy and for influencing public opinion was important. _____

_____

4. Were you or any other group members tempted to be biased in your presentation of information to the government or to the public? Why? How will this knowledge help you evaluate the information distributed and the activities of actual interest groups? _____

_____

_____

Your Role in the Simulation ★★★★★★★★★★★★★★★★★★★★★★★★★★★★★★★★★★★

5. How well do you think you performed your role in the simulation? Could you have done anything better? Explain your answer. _____

_____

6. Identify the three most important things you learned from participating in this simulation.

- _____

- _____

- _____

7. Write a brief paragraph that explains how this simulation helped you learn more about interest groups.

_____

_____

_____

Name _____ Date _____ Class _____

Government Simulations and Debates

Simulation 6: An Interest Group

DIRECTIONS Complete the profile to help you develop your simulated interest group.

INTEREST GROUP PROFILE

Name: _____

Type of Interest Group: _____

Membership: _____

Chief Areas of Concern: _____

_____

_____

_____

General Goals: _____

_____

_____

_____

Specific Policy Objectives: _____

_____

_____

Strategies for Influencing Government Policy: _____

_____

_____

_____

Strategies for Influencing Public Opinion: _____

_____

_____

_____

Government Simulations and Debates

Debate 7: American Lives on the Line?

The armed forces of the United States are well-trained, well-equipped, and dedicated. There is, however, a serious dispute about when these troops should be put into the field. Since the end of the Cold War, the United States has increasingly committed troops to carry out humanitarian missions or to enforce peace agreements.

Is this a proper use of our armed forces? While many U.S. citizens think so, others disagree. They object to risking young American lives in places where the interests of the American people are not directly at stake. The argument goes to the heart of the questions about U.S. foreign policy and the international order that has arisen in the wake of the Cold War.

DIRECTIONS Complete the steps below to learn about both sides of this issue. You will research and debate this resolution:

Resolved: The United States should commit troops to carry out humanitarian missions even when the safety and security of the United States is not at risk.

Step 1. **Learn About the Issue** Begin by conducting research about the recent use of the U.S. military. Identify missions relevant to the resolution, find out about their goals, and evaluate their successes and failures. Consult your textbook, other books, periodical articles, and other appropriate sources. The chart in the front of this book will guide you in your research. Your goal is to find or develop on your own at least three arguments for answering the resolution in the affirmative and three arguments against it. As you identify each argument, make sure you take note of the statistics, quotations, and other evidence that support each argument. Make sure you also develop responses or refutations to the arguments on both sides.

Step 2. **Debate the Issue** Once you have completed your research, organize two teams: a team that will support the resolution, and a team that will oppose it. The debate will consist of presentations, questions, and rebuttals. Refer to page iv in the front of this booklet for a description of the debate format.

Step 3. **Reflect on the Issue**

DIRECTIONS On a separate sheet of paper complete the following:

1. Write a paragraph that explains your opinion about the resolution.

2. How do you think the United States' experience in the Vietnam conflict might affect the debates over troop commitments?

3. **Activity:** Interview a current or retired member of the armed forces to find out his or her opinion about the resolution. Be sure to ask whether and how the interviewee's military experience may have influenced his or her position.

Simulation 7: Teacher Strategy

ACHIEVING CUTS IN THE FEDERAL BUDGET

In this simulation, students will assume the roles of members of a federal department or agency reviewing its budget in an attempt to help reduce the federal budget deficit.

PURPOSE ★★★★★★★★★★★★★★★★★★★

Serious economic, humanitarian, safety, security, political, and cultural issues come into play as people in the U.S. and their leaders consider how best to spend hundreds of billions of dollars of federal revenue. Students' understanding of the federal budget and the budget process is critical to their overall understanding of U.S. government and citizenship.

OBJECTIVES ★★★★★★★★★★★★★★★★★

By participating in this simulation, students will:
• explain how the federal budget is determined
• realize the challenges of attempting to reduce federal expenditures
• analyze the costs and benefits of specific changes in the federal budget

TIME REQUIRED ★★★★★★★★★★★★★

This simulation activity is designed to be conducted over the course of one week (five class periods, plus out-of-class preparation time), in conjunction with student reading and studying of the government spending policy. You can abbreviate the time required by doing much of the preparatory work yourself. Consider devoting at least two class periods to the simulation to allow adequate preparation, participation, and evaluation time.

MATERIALS ★★★★★★★★★★★★★★★★★★

• Student copies of Activity Sheets 7A, 7B, 7C, 7D, and 7E
• Folders
• Excerpts from *The Budget of the United States Government*

TEACHING TIPS ★★★★★★★★★★★★★

• Help students select a department or agency whose budget is relatively simple, but whose activities are familiar.

• Make sure students understand that reducing or eliminating items in the budget can have indirect, as well as direct, and long-term, as well as short-term, consequences. For example, reducing salaries would have the direct and short-term consequence of saving money, but might have the long-term effect of reducing the quality of staff. Indirect effects might introduce the reduction in quality of the programs administered, resulting in logistical and service problems for the public.

• If students use the Internet to access the federal budget, you might wish to have them download the appropriate figures into a spreadsheet for manipulation. The entire budget is available online at http://www.access.gpo.gov.

PROCEDURE ★★★★★★★★★★★★★★★★★

Introduce the Simulation Use Activity Sheet 7A (Background Brief) as the basis for this lesson. Make sure students understand the role that federal spending and deficits play in current political, economic, and cultural discourse.

Prepare for the Simulation Use Activity Sheet 7B (Preparing for the Simulation) as the basis for this lesson. Make sure students understand the point in the budget process that they will be simulating. Consider distributing Activity Sheet 7C (Conducting the Simulation) in advance to help students prepare for the simulation.

Conduct the Simulation Use Activity Sheets 7C (Conducting the Simulation) and 7E to emphasize the importance of the cost-benefit analyses in reaching decisions. Discourage students from making across-the-board cuts of a specific percentage in each category.

Review the Simulation Use Activity Sheet 7D (Reviewing the Simulation) as the basis for this lesson. The sheet functions well as a homework activity.

Name _____ Date _____ Class _____

Government Simulations and Debates

Simulation 7: Achieving Cuts in the Federal Budget

⭐ **DIRECTIONS** You will participate in a simulated budget meeting of a committee in a federal department or agency. To help you prepare, read the Background Brief. Then answer the questions.

★★★★★★★★★★★★★★★★★★★★★ | Background Brief | ★★★★★★★★★★★★★★★★★★★★★

When speaking about the federal budget, we find numbers so large that we have difficulty imagining that much money.

Almost as incomprehensible is the way that the federal budget is prepared and implemented by the president, the Office of Management and Budget, the Council of Economic Advisers, the secretary of the treasury, every federal department and agency, all the members of Congress, House and Senate Budget Committees, the Congressional Budget Office, and so on. The process takes more than a year to complete.

Most U.S. citizens do not understand the complex budgeting process. Yet the issues surrounding the budget are among the most important confronting our country. Are we spending enough on education? Is the government wasting money? Should the government fund programs to which many U.S. citizens object? Is government spending hurting or helping the economy?

The federal budget has been on everyone's mind because the federal government spends more than it takes in. By the late 1990s the annual deficit exceeded $100 billion, and the national debt exceeded $5 trillion. When the government borrows money to finance its debt, it reduces the amount of money in the economy that consumers and businesses are able to borrow. Tight money can retard economic growth and increase interest rates. Moreover, high, deficit-level spending fuels inflation and raises taxes.

The debt also costs the government money. When the government runs a deficit, it has to borrow money and pay interest on the loans. By the late 1990s interest payments accounted for more than one of every five dollars the government spent—nearly the amount spent on national defense. If the debt were eliminated, billions of dollars could be made available to spend on worthy government programs.

As complex as the federal budget is, there are basically two ways to control it: increase revenues or decrease spending. Since increasing revenues means increasing taxes, many U.S. citizens demand that the federal government decrease spending. But decreasing spending is not simple. When government departments or agencies must reduce spending, they face tough choices.

★★

1. Why do many U.S. citizens lack a complete understanding of the issues surrounding the federal budget?

2. What important national issues are associated with the federal budget?

3. What are some harmful effects of the federal budget deficit?

4. What are the two basic ways to eliminate the federal budget deficit?

Government Simulations and Debates

Simulation 7: Achieving Cuts in the Federal Budget

DIRECTIONS You will participate in a simulation of a federal department or agency committee meeting. The goal of the committee is to reduce the department's or agency's budget. To help you prepare, complete the steps below.

Step 1. **Prepare a Simulation Folder** Use a folder to organize the various papers you will need for your simulation. Your folder should include any activity sheets (such as this one) your teacher hands out, research materials, and notes you take. Update your folder as you proceed.

Step 2. **Choose a Federal Department or Agency** Your basic task will be to review the budget of a particular federal department or agency. Work with your classmates to choose one to consider. You may select any one, so identify the department or agency that is most interesting to you.

Step 3. **Locate a Copy of Your Selected Department's or Agency's Budget** The federal budget is detailed in a four-volume set entitled *The Budget of the United States Government*. Titles in the set include *Analytical Perspectives, Historical Tables, Budgetary Systems and Concepts*, an *Appendix*. The entire set is available at major public libraries and at university libraries.

Direct your attention to the *Appendix*, in which specific expenditures of the various federal departments and agencies are detailed. Find the budget for your selected department or agency and make at least two copies to work with.

Step 4. **Organize Two or More Committees** You will assume the role of department or agency leaders working in committees whose task is to reduce expenditures as part of a government-wide effort to reduce the federal budget deficit. Form two or more committees to achieve this task. Each committee should consist of at least three students.

Step 5. **Hold an Initial Committee Meeting and Plan Your Approach** Each committee should meet to plan the way in which it will decide on budgetary reductions or cuts. Questions each committee must answer include: What percentage cut in the budget is our goal? How will our committee work? For example, will individual committee members each analyze specific parts of the budget, or will we all work together? Will we have a committee chair person who will weigh proposals and make final decisions, or will we seek consensus? What criteria will we use in determining whether to cut specific items from the budget? Outline your planned approach on a separate sheet of paper.

Government Simulations and Debates

Simulation 7: Achieving Cuts in the Federal Budget

DIRECTIONS You will experience the choices and high stakes that government departments and agencies face while trying to reduce spending. Complete the steps below. Use the space below each step to take notes during the simulation.

Step 1. **Meet to Reduce the Budget** The specific way in which your committee operates is up to you. Remember your goal is to cut the budget as much as possible.

Step 2. **Evaluate Each Item in the Budget** Consider your budget on a line-by-line basis. For each budget item, conduct a cost-benefit analysis. In other words, weigh the costs of including the expenditure against the benefits it achieves. Is it worth the money? Also consider the costs of *not* including the item in the budget. Is saving the money worth the drawback of eliminating the expenditure? To help you conduct these analyses, complete Activity Sheet 7E.

Step 3. **Propose Cuts** As you evaluate budget items, develop a list of proposed cuts. For each item on the list, specify how much money will be saved, both in dollar terms and as a percentage of your department or agency's budget. Also specify your rationale for cutting that item, addressing the drawbacks associated with eliminating the expenditure.

Step 4. **Prepare a Final Report** Organize the list you prepared in Step 3 into a final budget-cutting proposal. Submit it to your teacher and classmates.

Step 5. **Compare and Contrast the Proposals** Weigh the various committees' proposals against one another. Compare and contrast them to determine which proposal seems to offer the most advantages and the fewest disadvantages. To help you reach these decisions, consider these questions:

- **Cost Cutting** Which proposal succeeds in reducing the budget by the greatest overall amount?

- **Budget Item Selection** Which proposal is most effective in reducing or deleting the least important items in the budget?

- **Cost-Benefit Analyses** Which proposal is the result of the most detailed and thoughtful considerations of costs and benefits? Are long-term as well as short-term consequences considered? Are indirect as well as direct consequences considered?

- **Political Acceptability** Which proposal is most likely to receive support from the people and their representatives in Congress?

Name _____ Date _____ Class _____

Simulation 7: Achieving Cuts in the Federal Budget

⭐ **DIRECTIONS** To help you get the most out of the simulation, think carefully about your experience in the simulation as you answer the questions below.

The Simulation ★★★

1. What was the best thing about the simulation? What was the worse thing about it? Explain your answers. _____

_____

_____

2. Evaluate the realism of your simulation. In other words, how well do you think you and your classmates re-created actual federal budget-making processes? _____

_____

_____

3. Why was cost-benefit analysis of specific budget items necessary? _____

_____

4. In what ways did long-term and indirect consequences of reducing or eliminating expenditures affect your decisions? _____

_____

5. Why is cutting federal spending difficult? _____

_____

_____

Your Role in the Simulation ★★★★★★★★★★★★★★★★★★★★★★★★★★★★★★★★★★★★★★★

6. How well do you think you performed your role in the simulation? Could you have done anything better? Explain your answer. _____

_____

_____

7. Identify the three most important things you learned from participating in this simulation.

  • _____

  • _____

  • _____

Name _____ Date _____ Class _____

Simulation 7: Achieving Cuts in the Federal Budget

DIRECTIONS Use the chart to help you evaluate the costs and benefits of reducing or eliminating specific budget items.

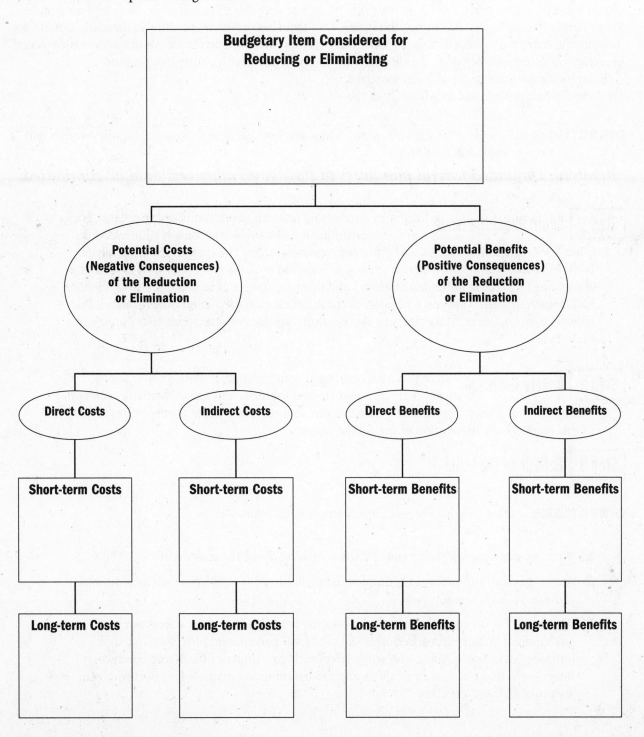

Government Simulations and Debates

Debate 8: Federal Mandate versus States' Rights?

From the very beginning, questions about whether the states, or the national government, should wield power in critical areas have been subject to serious debate. In the last century, the issues surrounding states' rights helped cause the Civil War. In recent years, they have helped to decide elections.

Today the debate focuses on unfunded mandates. The federal government, under the authority of the Constitution, issues countless mandates, or orders, to state governments. In recent years the number of mandates has increased while the federal funding for them has decreased, resulting in mandates that are not supported by federal funds. Is this a reasonable federal policy, or does it violate states' rights?

DIRECTIONS — Complete the steps below to learn about both sides of this issue. You will research and debate this resolution:

Resolved: Unfunded federal mandates to state governments should be eliminated.

Step 1. **Learn About the Issue** Begin by conducting research about unfunded mandates. Focus on the constitutional issues involved. Consult your textbook, other books, periodical articles, and other appropriate sources. The chart at the front of this book will guide you in your research. Your goal is to find or develop on your own at least three arguments for keeping unfunded mandates and three arguments against them. As you identify each argument, make sure you take notes of the statistics, quotations, and other evidence that support each argument. Make sure you also develop responses or refutations to the arguments on both sides.

Step 2. **Debate the Issue** Once you have completed your research, organize two teams: a team that will support the resolution, and a team that will oppose it. The debate will consist of presentations, questions, and rebuttals. Refer to page iv in the front of this booklet for a description of the debate format.

Step 3. **Reflect on the Issue**

DIRECTIONS — On a separate sheet of paper complete the following:

1. Write a paragraph explaining your personal opinion about the resolution.

2. Assess the constitutionality of unfunded mandates. In your view does the Constitution allow or prohibit them?

3. **Activity:** How do unfunded mandates from the federal government affect your local government? With your teacher, create a list of local government officials affected by unfunded mandates. Decide who will contact each government official and conduct an interview to find out how he or she is affected by unfunded mandates. Report what you learn to the rest of the class.

Government Simulations and Debates

Simulation 8: Teacher Strategy

A MOCK PUBLIC HEARING

In this simulation students will assume the roles of local government officials and interested citizens as they simulate a public hearing on an issue of local concern.

PURPOSE ★★★★★★★★★★★★★★★★★★★★★

The local level of government is where U.S. citizens, as a rule, have the greatest potential for influencing public policy. For these reasons, student simulation of the dynamics of local government decision making is a vital part of their learning experience with U.S. government.

OBJECTIVES ★★★★★★★★★★★★★★★★★★

By participating in this simulation, students will:
• identify the type, powers, and functions of their community's government
• evaluate the role of citizen input in creating local policies
• analyze the process and effectiveness of local government decision making

TIME REQUIRED ★★★★★★★★★★★★★★★★

This simulation activity is designed to be conducted over the course of one week (five class periods, plus out-of-class preparation time) in conjunction with student reading and studying about local government. You can abbreviate the time required by doing much of the preparatory work yourself. Consider devoting at least two class periods to the simulation.

MATERIALS ★★★★★★★★★★★★★★★★★★★★

• Student copies of Activity Sheets 8A, 8B, 8C, 8D, and 8E
• Folders
• Research materials (local newspapers and local government documents)

TEACHING TIPS ★★★★★★★★★★★★★★★★

• Guide students into selecting a topic for their simulation that is timely, reported in the local media, and controversial. Emphasize the importance of research to make the simulation realistic and worthwhile.
• Remind students to develop their characters fully and to stay in character during the simulation.
• Consider taking students on a field trip to observe an actual public hearing to prepare them for the simulation.

PROCEDURE ★★★★★★★★★★★★★★★★★★★★

Introduce the Simulation Use Activity Sheet 8A (Background Brief) as the basis for this lesson. Guide students in a broad discussion of local government powers, narrowing the focus to how these powers are manifested in your community. Bring or have students bring to class newspaper reports of recent local government actions.

Prepare for the Simulation Use Activity Sheets 8B (Preparing for the Simulation) and 8E as the basis for this lesson. Make sure that students identify an interesting issue, and stress the importance of thorough research. Use Activity Sheet 8E to profile the local government body students will simulate. Consider distributing Activity Sheet 8C (Conducting the Simulation) in advance to help students prepare for the simulation.

Conduct the Simulation Use Activity Sheet 8C (Conducting the Simulation) as the basis for this lesson. Make sure that students stay in character and follow the rules under which the actual government body holds hearings. Step in when necessary to keep the simulation realistic, but strive for a hands-off approach.

Review the Simulation Use Activity Sheet 8D (Reviewing the Simulation) as a homework activity, or as a guide for a classroom discussion.

Name _____ Date _____ Class _____

Government Simulations and Debates

Activity Sheet 8A   Background Brief

Simulation 8: A Mock Public Hearing

DIRECTIONS You will participate in a simulated public hearing before a local government body. To help you prepare, read the Background Brief. Then answer the questions.

★ ★ ★ ★ ★ ★ ★ ★ ★ ★ ★ ★ ★ ★ ★ ★ | Background Brief | ★ ★ ★ ★ ★ ★ ★ ★ ★ ★ ★ ★ ★ ★ ★ ★

Nowhere is the power of the people more evident than at the local level of government. The average citizen's chances of being heard in a local government body approaches 100 percent. The issues closest to our day-to-day lives—local issues—are also the ones in which we have the most voice.

The voice of citizens is strong at the local level; one local citizen, speaking before a city council, can convince council members to enact, change, or revoke a law. Groups of citizens, acting in concert, armed with petitions, and speaking with one voice, can have even greater influence.

Although local governments lack the glamour of the national government, they make decisions on vital issues such as police and fire protection and social services. They plan and maintain roads, manage traffic, and shape our communities through zoning laws. They provide clean water, parks and cultural centers, sewage and sanitation systems—all of the things that directly affect our quality of life.

Local governments usually fall into four basic categories—the county, the township, the municipality, and the special district. Not all exist in every state, and their powers vary from state to state. Moreover, each of these basic types has several subtypes. In the end, however, they all provide vital services and create the platform where grassroots movements have their strongest say in the U.S. government.

★ ★

1. Why is the influence of grassroots movements strongest at the local government level?

2. Explain the statement, "Each local government is unique, but all local governments are basically the same."

3. Identify at least three ways that decisions of your local government have affected your life.

4. Construct an organizational chart to show the structure of one of the basic categories of local government. Identify the offices in each subdivision and the person who holds that position in your community.

Government Simulations and Debates

Simulation 8: A Mock Public Hearing

⭐ **DIRECTIONS** You will participate in a simulated public hearing before a local government body. To help you prepare, complete the steps below.

Step 1. **Prepare a Simulation Folder** Use a folder to organize the various papers you will need for your simulation. Your folder should include any activity sheets (such as this one) your teacher hands out, research materials, and notes you take. Update your folder as you proceed.

Step 2. **Identify an Issue of Intense Local Concern** What are the current hot issues in your community? Property taxes? School board policy? Traffic? List at least three current issues. (Your local newspaper is the best source for this information.) Then consult with your classmates and choose one that you would like to use as the topic for your simulation.

_____

Step 3. **Identify the Relevant Local Government Body** Which local government body is most directly concerned with the issue you identified in Step 2? Identify the relevant local government body.

_____

Step 4. **Create a Profile of the Relevant Local Government Body** Contact local officials and consult your city charter or other relevant document to profile the local government body you will simulate. Use Activity Sheet 8E to record what you learn. Pay special attention to the rules for public hearings.

_____

Step 5. **Assign Roles** Using the profile you created in Step 4, determine which government officials need to be portrayed in your simulation, and decide which students will play each role. Conduct additional research to identify and assign roles for individual citizens, who may be part of a grassroots movement, and interest group representatives who will testify at the hearing.

_____

Step 6. **Prepare for Your Role** Thorough research is the key to this step. Study the history of the issue you have identified. Record the arguments and evidence various groups use to support their positions. Students portraying citizens and interest group representatives should prepare short presentations to give before the local government body. Students portraying government officials should prepare lists of questions to ask those who testify.

_____

Government Simulations and Debates

Simulation 8: A Mock Public Hearing

DIRECTIONS — In this simulation you will experience a public hearing firsthand. Your simulation will include role-playing representatives whom local government will hear, the citizens, and interest groups. Complete the steps below and use the space below each step to take notes during the simulation.

Step 1. **Arrange the Classroom** Organize the desks in the classroom to approximate the layout of the room in which actual public hearings are held.

_____

_____

Step 2. **Be Aware of Proper Procedure** Depending on the local government body you are simulating, the rules for holding the hearing will vary. Use the information you recorded on Activity Sheet 8E as a guide, and follow the actual rules as much as possible. Be aware of such things as the order in which business is conducted, time limits for those who testify, who chairs the meeting, and so on.

_____

_____

Step 3. **Hear Testimony** Make sure that all students have the chance to contribute to the simulation. Government officials and those who testify should challenge their opponents' positions and defend their own.

_____

_____

Step 4. **Reach a Decision** The government body should discuss the testimony and hold a vote to reach a decision. It should then issue its written decision, along with the reasons for that decision, to the class.

_____

_____

Step 5. **Evaluate the Meeting** Analyze the proceedings by considering the following questions in a classroom discussion:

- How responsive were the government officials to the statements of the citizens?

- Did individuals or representatives of groups seem to have more influence?

- Did officials seem to base their decisions on the public good or on political grounds?

Government Simulations and Debates

Simulation 8: A Mock Public Hearing

⭐ **DIRECTIONS** ➤ To help you get the most out of the simulation, think carefully about your experience in the simulation as you answer the questions below.

The Simulation ★★★

1. What was the best thing about the simulation? What was the worst thing about it? Explain.

_____

_____

_____

2. Evaluate the realism of your simulation. In other words, how accurately do you think you and your classmates re-created the events of an actual public hearing before a local government body?

_____

_____

_____

3. How did the action of the government body in your simulation compare to any actions taken by the actual government body? _____

_____

4. How efficient do you think the government body you simulated is? Is the decision-making process complex and burdensome, or is it streamlined? In what ways do you think the process could be improved?

_____

_____

Your Role in the Simulation ★★★★★★★★★★★★★★★★★★★★★★★★★★★★★★★★★

5. How well do you think you performed your role in the simulation? Could you have done anything better? Explain. _____

_____

6. Identify the three most important things you learned from participating in this simulation.

• _____

• _____

• _____

7. How has your participation in the simulation affected your feelings about your local government and your beliefs about the influence you might have over it? _____

_____

Name _____ Date _____ Class _____

Government Simulations and Debates

Activity Sheet 8E

Simulation 8: A Mock Public Hearing

⭐ **DIRECTIONS** Use the chart to help you create a profile of a local government body.

PROFILE OF A LOCAL GOVERNMENT BODY	
Name	
Type	
Organization	
Major Responsibilities	
Titles and Names of Major Officials	
Major Rules for Operation	

Government Simulations and Debates

Debate 9: Should China Be a Most Favored Nation?

Home to one out of every five people on earth, a major military power, and the leading Communist state in the world, China looms large on the horizon of U.S. foreign policy. Although the policy toward China has varied with the changing international situation, defining that policy has always been a critical challenge.

The Sino-American relationship is a delicate balance between economic and political concerns. These concerns converge in the debate over most favored

nation (MFN) status for China. Having most favored nation status makes trading with the United States easier. Many want to withhold MFN status for China in an effort to punish China for its dismal human rights record and to give China an incentive for reform. Others see keeping close economic ties to China as key to helping the U.S. economy while encouraging Chinese reform through trade.

DIRECTIONS Complete the steps below to learn about both sides of this issue. You will research and debate this resolution:

Resolved: The United States should grant China most favored nation status.

Step 1. **Learn About the Issue** Begin by conducting research to learn what MFN status is, how widely it is granted, and why and how it is granted and revoked. Consult your textbook, other books, periodical articles, and other sources. The chart in the front of this book will guide you in your research. Develop at least three arguments for granting MFN status to China and three arguments against it. Make sure to take notes of the statistics, quotations, and other evidence that supports each argument, and to develop refutations to the arguments on both sides.

Step 2. **Debate the Issue** Organize two teams: a team that will support the resolution, and a team that will oppose it. The debate will consist of presentations, questions, and rebuttals. Refer to page iv in the front of this booklet for a description of the debate format.

Step 3. **Reflect on the Issue**

DIRECTIONS On a separate sheet of paper complete the following:

1. Write a paragraph that identifies your opinion about the resolution and explain the reasons for your position.

2. The question of MFN status for China reflects a larger, common foreign policy question: Is it better to threaten countries with poor human rights records or keep close ties and engage them? Address this question in a paragraph.

3. **Activity:** Identify a trading partner to which the United States has recently granted MFN status. Conduct research and chart the trade between the two countries in the years before and after the status was granted. Assess the impact of the change in MFN status on trade, in terms of both imports and exports of both countries.

Simulation 9: Teacher Strategy

A MOCK SECURITY COUNCIL MEETING

In this simulation, students will act as members of the United Nations Security Council as they consider an international crisis in curbing terrorism and propose, debate, and vote on solutions to the crisis.

PURPOSE ★★★★★★★★★★★★★★★★★★

As the preeminent international organization, the United Nations (UN) has played a major role in worldwide events for more than 50 years. With the end of the Cold War, the UN has taken on an even greater prominence. The potentially most powerful organ of the UN is the Security Council, of which the United States is a permanent member. There is little doubt the Security Council will be a major factor on the international scene for many years to come, so student understanding and appreciation of the Security Council's role, power, and limits is critical to broader understanding of international developments.

OBJECTIVES ★★★★★★★★★★★★★★★★

By participating in this simulation, students will:
- analyze the role of the Security Council in helping to solve an international crisis
- explain how the UN Security Council reaches decisions
- evaluate the effectiveness of the Security Council

TIME REQUIRED ★★★★★★★★★★★★★★

This simulation activity is designed to be conducted over the course of one week (five class periods, plus out-of-class preparations time), in conjunction with student reading and studying of the United Nations. You can abbreviate the time required by doing much of the preparatory work yourself. Consider devoting at least two class periods to the simulation to allow adequate preparation, participation, and evaluation time.

MATERIALS ★★★★★★★★★★★★★★★★★

- Student copies of Activity Sheets 9A, 9B, 9C, 9D, and 9E
- Folders

TEACHING TIPS ★★★★★★★★★★★★★

- Have students select a country whose interests are directly affected by international terrorism, such as Great Britain, France, or the United States to propose a resolution to the Security Council aimed at curbing the problem of international terrorism.
- Emphasize the importance of student-delegates acting from the standpoints of the countries they represent.
- Allow students to dress in appropriate clothes (dress clothes), and use props such as tables and charts, to make the simulation more realistic and colorful.

PROCEDURE ★★★★★★★★★★★★★★★★★

Introduce the Simulation Use Activity Sheet 9A (Background Brief) as the basis for this lesson. Newspaper reports of recent Security Council actions may serve as the basis for the simulation.

Prepare for the Simulation Use Activity Sheet 9B (Preparing for the Simulation) as the basis for this lesson. The ideal group size for this activity is 15 students (one per country). Allow students adequate time to conduct their research before the actual simulation. Consider distributing Activity Sheet 9C (Conducting the Simulation) in advance to help students prepare for the simulation.

Conduct the Simulation Use Activity Sheet 9C (Conducting the Simulation) as the basis for this lesson. It is critical that students' proposals, arguments, and voting reflect the national interests of the countries they are representing. Step in to keep the simulations as realistic as possible, but strive for a hands-off approach as much as possible.

Review the Simulation Use Activity Sheets 9D (Reviewing the Simulation) and 9E as the basis for this lesson. The sheets function well as homework activities, or you can use them as guides for a classroom discussion about the simulation.